PRAISE FOR
The Anthropocene

CU00665789

"With thorough and easily readable explanations, this book is a great contribution to helping the general public understand the gravity of the challenges facing the world's oceans."
—Rashid Sumaila, Ph.D., Professor of Ocean and Fisheries, University of British Columbia

"A fascinating and extremely well written account of the environmental mess we have created for ourselves and some provocative suggestions on how we might start a clean-up. Read it and learn!"
—Michael Ruse, Ph.D., Professor of Philosophy of Science, Florida State University

"...a clearly readable, thoughtful and deeply felt exploration of how complex, growing human forces are now having overwhelming impacts on the Earth System, and bringing about the increasingly unstable planetary conditions of the Anthropocene."
—Jan Zalasiewicz, Ph.D., Professor of Palaeobiology, University of Leicester

"Important. Impactful. Surprising. ...undeniably informative ...right near the top [of] the best books I've read this year."
—*Independent Book Review*

"Engrossing ... accessible ... comprehensive..."
—*Foreword* Clarion Reviews

"...compelling... A refreshingly optimistic environmental survey."
—*Kirkus Reviews*

"Written in clear language and backed up by solid evidence at every turn... *The Anthropocene Epoch* explains the current climate change crisis and sets it in its various contexts—geological, historical, and sociopolitical."
—*IndieReader Review*

The Anthropocene Epoch

The

Anthropocene Epoch

When Humans Changed the World

Bruce Glass

PUBLISHING

The Anthropocene Epoch

Copyright © Bruce Glass 2021

All rights reserved. No part of this publication may be used or reproduced in any manner without the written permission of the publisher, with the exception of brief quotations embodied in critical articles or reviews.

For information, write the DBG Publishing at 8605 Concord Trace, Houston, Texas 77055, or visit www.dbgpublishing.com or www.theanthropoceneepoch.com.

ISBN-13: 978-0-578-99530-4

ISBN-10: 0-578-99530-1

ISBN (ebook): 978-0-578-31820-2

Library of Congress Control Number: 2021919525

Manufactured in the United States

First Edition: 2021

For Our Children

Contents

Introduction

Have you ever wondered why penguins are found only in or near Antarctica and the Southern Hemisphere, not in the Arctic or the Northern Hemisphere? The climatic conditions and the requisite resources are similar enough that penguins could flourish in Norway, Iceland, Greenland, Alaska, or Siberia and beyond.[1] So, why are they absent? Humans.

The word "penguin" was originally used in association with a Northern Hemisphere flightless bird called the great auk. Standing as much as two and a half feet tall, sporting black and white plumage and diminutive wings that had evolved for swimming, they resembled some of the penguins we know today (Though they were from a wholly different family of birds.[2]).

Before human populations had reduced their numbers, great auks once flourished around the coasts of the North Atlantic, as far north as Norway, Iceland, and over to Newfoundland, and as far south as Gibraltar and the Florida Peninsula. When European explorers and traders began regular ventures to North America early in the sixteenth century, the birds could still be found in abundance on and around Iceland and on tiny Funk Island off the coast of Newfoundland.[3]

Though fast swimmers, like today's penguins, they would waddle ashore to breed and incubate their eggs, leaving them very easy to catch. Explorers filled their ships with vast numbers of great auks to be used for the birds' meat and feathers. Their oily bodies even made them suitable as fuel for fires.[4]

As was common in those years, little thought was given to conservation or cruelty. An English seaman named Aaron Thomas, who had sailed to Newfoundland aboard the HMS Boston, reported in his 1794 journal,

> If you come for their feathers you do not give yourself the trouble of killing them, but lay hold of one and pluck the best of the Feathers. You then turn the poor Penguin adrift, with his skin half naked and torn off, to perish at his leisure.[5]

The last great auks to be seen alive were in June 1844, when a small group of sightseers rowed to a tiny island off the coast of Iceland. By then, the birds' rarity had made them valuable to collectors. With rough seas and a dangerously rocky coastline, only three men managed to get ashore. Upon seeing the humans, a single pair of auks made an effort to run, but were quickly caught and strangled. The single egg the pair had been incubating was evidently cracked in the struggle, so it was left behind.[6]

The story of the great auk is but one among many such tales of human history. Similar fates befell the dodo bird, the giant moa among other moa species, the massive elephant bird, the Carolina parakeet, the Zanzibar leopard, the Caribbean monk seal, the atlas bear, the sea mink, Steller's sea cow, the West Africa black rhinoceros, the baiji white dolphin, the passenger pigeon (the last one of those, named "Martha," died in the Cincinnati Zoo in 1914), and a great many more species that were extinguished by human consumption, sport, or carelessness.

Superstition, greed, callousness, and short-sightedness today are threatening the extinction of many more species. Economic growth in Asia has been accompanied by greater demand for rhinoceros-horn (foolishly believed to be an aphrodisiac and a cure for cancer) and for ivory (seen as a status symbol and an artistic investment). Since 2008 in South Africa alone, more than nine thousand increasingly rare rhinos have been poached just for their horns. Tens of thousands of African elephants are killed each year by poachers, some of whom have been known to use automatic weapons to wipe out entire herds, including the calves, just to steal the ivory.[7]

Day after day, Chinese fishermen in the South China Sea near the Philippines are intentionally destroying reefs that took five to ten thousand years to form, in order to harvest rare, hundred-year-old giant clams.[8] New wealth in China is making trade in endangered species, including the critically endangered Hawksbill sea turtle, more lucrative than fishing.

Most species extinctions resulting from human activity, however, are not the direct result of harvesting, but are merely the side effects of expanding human civilization. As we deplete fisheries, clear old-growth forests, expand cities and agricultural tracts, and build a multitude of roads all over the planet, ecological habitats are altered, severed, or totally lost, leaving the species that depend on them to adapt or perish. Many have perished.

Even the plants, animals, bacteria, fungi, and viruses that humans have carried (intentionally or inadvertently) around the world have affected the viability of a great many local species. For the last two centuries, growing emissions of greenhouse gases have altered the atmosphere in ways that add stresses to a great many species, not to mention our own.

Though it may be difficult for many of us to imagine, we are witnessing our planet's sixth mass extinction event—an event preceded by five similarly devastating mass extinction episodes over the course of the 3.7-billion-year history of life on Earth—episodes such as the so-called K-T extinction 65 million years ago, when an asteroid impact resulted in the demise of about three-quarters of Earth's organisms, including all non-avian dinosaurs.

This is not the first time a phylum of life has affected the planet in such a dramatic way. As we will see in Chapter 1, it was the photosynthesizing activity of a great volume of cyanobacteria (blue-green algae) over a period of some 3 billion years that first produced the oxygen that animals breathe and the ozone layer in Earth's upper atmosphere that protects terrestrial life from UV radiation. This too might be difficult to imagine, until we come to recognize just how thin (and vulnerable) Earth's atmosphere is. This time, however, it has not been a phylum's activity over billions of years. It has been a single species that has dramatically changed the planet over just a few thousand, hundred, and even tens of years.

We are living in the midst of the "Anthropocene" (human affected and recent) geological epoch—a term not yet officially adopted, but aptly proposed by Nobel Prize winning Dutch atmospheric chemist Paul Crutzen[9] because:

- Nearly half of our planet's land surface area has been altered by human activity.
- Almost all of the world's major rivers have been dammed or diverted.
- More nitrogen in fertilizer is applied by humans than is fixed naturally in all terrestrial ecosystems.
- Commercial fishing removes more than 25 percent of fish in upwelling ocean regions, and 35 percent of primary fish production in continental shelf waters.
- Humans use more than half of the world's easily accessible fresh water.
- Through fossil fuel combustion, agricultural production, and deforestation, humans have significantly altered the composition of Earth's atmosphere.

So, the questions at hand are: Is this something to be truly concerned about, and is there anything we can realistically do about it anyway?

Yes, and perhaps.

The following pages are intended to offer readers some historical perspective on how we (humankind) have changed our planet. They are also intended to bolster what many people already know about how our continuing activities are putting our own way of life at risk—to stress the urgency of the problems of deforestation, wild habitat destruction, resource depletion, species extinction, and climate change.

Many of us tend to overlook how much the world has changed even during our short lifetimes. Marine biology Professor Daniel Pauly of the University of British Columbia has described a phenomenon he calls "shifting baseline syndrome." Professor Pauly used the term to describe how marine biologists fail to adequately recognize changes in fish species sizes as a result of depletion over a few decades. But the idea is more universal than that. At each stage of our lives, we tend to see the world around us as "normal," not really remembering how much different it was when we were children.[10]

For example, the population of Texas today is nearly four times what it was in 1950, and many of us who have lived in Texas since the 1950s may not feel like things are all that much different. But they are. As much as we like open spaces and pristine woodlands, forests, and beaches, we may not think about how much of those have been lost. We don't often think about the loss of a small-town feeling in places like Boerne or Dripping Springs, much less Cedar Park, Grapevine, or Sugar Land—once small towns, now consumed by metropolises. We may not think much about how fireflies and horny toads* were once common, but are now hard to find. Most of us don't think about the loss of ocelots and pronghorns, or the proliferation of invasive and destructive wild hogs.[11] We tend not to remember how many more stars we could see at night as children in many parts of the state.

It is a common phenomenon sometimes called "change blindness" or "creeping amnesia." It is akin to the proverbial frog in

---

* Horny toads are also called "horned toads" or "horned frogs," but they are neither. They are lizards—magnificent lizards that resemble little Triceratops dinosaurs and can shoot blood from their eyes. How cool is that?!

a pot of soon-to-be boiling water not realizing how hot it is getting. We tend not to realize just how much of nature we have lost during our lifetimes and, with our collective amnesia as a society, how much has been lost over the last 100 or even 150 years—less than a blink of an eye in terms of geologic time. We should, however, so we can see how much our children have lost and see what is at stake for their future.

There is little doubt that human ingenuity, particularly that of capitalist motivations, can make the necessary accommodations for a great deal more population growth and infrastructure development. Most developed nations can remain sufficiently fed and even comfortable. But what will be the character of the world in which we choose to live? Do we not also wish for the wellbeing of *all* the world's populations? Do we not have a stake in preserving the natural state of our own surroundings and resources? Will we choose to live in a synthetic *Brave New World*? Or will we work to protect the natural Earth from which humankind arose to ponder the universe and our own role and accountability within it?

We may do well to remember the words that have been commonly attributed to Chief Seattle of the nineteenth-century Duwamish Tribe of indigenous peoples of the American Pacific Northwest:[12]

> This we know: The Earth does not belong to man—man belongs to the Earth. All things are connected like the blood that unites us all. Man did not weave the web of life. He is merely a strand in it. Whatever he does to the web, he does to himself.

1

A Little Natural History

The planet we call home is a wonderful place to live. It is so well suited to all our needs, providing our food and water, the air we breathe, the warmth we require, and all of the raw materials necessary for our shelter and our prosperity. In addition to finding life's sustenance in it, we find great beauty and inspiration in our world. This, of course, is not because it was made for us. It is because we were made for it. But, let us start at the beginning.

Some four and a half billion years ago, planet Earth began as a glob of convulsing molten rock, its rotational axis tilted from the plane of its orbit around the sun as the result of its collision with a massive asteroid or protoplanet—a tilt that would come to dictate a cycle of seasons and the ocean currents that affect climates. The remnants of that collision had coalesced to form the moon.

The early moon was at least 18 times closer, and Earth was spinning much faster, with about five-hour days. The drag of the moon's gravitational pull on the world and its oceans created tides and has, over those 4.5 billion years, slowed our planet down to the 24-hour days with which we are familiar.[1]

Iron in the boiling mass was drawn by gravity to Earth's core. Then, as the planet cooled, a crust began to form and water vapor and other gases (mostly hydrogen) escaped and began to form an atmosphere.

After the planet's surface had cooled to below 212 degrees Fahrenheit (100 degrees Celsius), liquid water rained down for many centuries, forming the primeval sea by about 3.8 billion years ago.[2] The young Earth was also regularly bombarded by icy comets, adding to its waters.

Then, after another 100 million years, the first life emerged on the floor of that sea, probably within or next to volcanic hydro-thermal vents. By whatever means life may have begun, it soon speciated into prokaryotic (simple-cell), anaerobic (living in the absence of oxygen) organisms called cyanobacteria (or blue-green algae).[3]

After another 1.5 billion years, more complex eukaryotic cells had evolved. These are the type of cells that would later evolve into multicellular organisms, but not for another 600 million years. The fossil record tells us that for more than 3 billion years—some three-quarters of the history of life on Earth—single-cell organisms, mostly cyanobacteria, were the only living things on the planet. (See the geological time scale on page 31.)

The existence of that cyanobacteria is one of the most con-sequential events in the history of life. It was crucial to setting the stage for our own existence, and it provides us with a clear example of how life itself can dramatically affect the chemistry and the character of our planet.

Cyanobacteria produce oxygen as a by-product of photo-synthesis, adding oxygen (O_2) to the ocean and to the atmosphere—oxygen that animals would later come to utilize for respiration. After about 3 billion years of photosynthesis, enough oxygen had been produced to form a layer of ozone (O_3) in the upper atmosphere. The ozone layer filters out much of the ultraviolet radiation that emanates from the sun. It was only after the ozone layer had become sufficiently protective that life's colonization of land became possible, about 444 million years ago. Just as that colonization had begun, however, life on Earth experienced the first of its six catastrophic extinction events. (We'll get to that in a moment.)

After the first appearance of life, the diversity of living cells very slowly increased through evolutionary processes. With the emergence of multi-cellular organisms, around 635 million years ago, the pace picked up significantly. Then, what has been termed the "Cambrian Explosion" occurred about 540 million years ago.

The discovery of the fossils of creatures that lived in the Cambrian geological period (542 to 490 million years ago) appears to show a sudden[4] (in only a few million years) increase in the sizes and shapes of animal forms. These included brachiopods with shells like those of today's oysters or clams, and a wide variety of arthropods with jointed exoskeletons (the ancestors of crustaceans, spiders and, eventually, insects).

The most famous of the Cambrian period arthropods was an extensive diversity of trilobites, so named because of their three-lobed form. These fascinating creatures were so successful that they evolved into more than 20,000 species and lived in all the world's oceans for more than 260 million years. They even survived the first two of Earth's six mass extinction events, though their numbers were dramatically reduced and well over half of trilobite species were lost in each of those devastating episodes. The time in history of the Cambrian geological period and the subsequent Ordovician period is often called the "*Age of Trilobites.*"

Building on the dramatic speciation of the Cambrian, the Ordovician period (485 to 444 million years ago) also experienced a great blossoming of diversity among marine species in Earth's vast seas. Among the new creatures were squid-like nautiloids, a predatory tentacled mollusk. Nautiloids used grasping tentacles to capture prey. Another group of predators were the conodonts. Having gone extinct long ago, conodonts are known only from a few complete fossils along with an abundance of fossilized teeth. The creatures were finned eel-like animals with large eyes for locating their prey.

During the Ordovician period, most of the world's landmasses, including what would later become the continents of Africa, South America, Australia, and Antarctica, came together to form the supercontinent Gondwana, which drifted southward throughout the period until arriving at the South Pole. A second supercontinent called Laurentia included the land-mass that would eventually become North America, though it was partly under water at that time. Throughout most of the Ordovician, Earth's climate was quite warm, with sea levels as much as 600 meters (1,970 feet) above those of today.

Toward the latter part of the period a few primitive plants and a few hard-bodied arthropods began to appear on land. These arthropods included the ancient ancestors of horseshoe crabs, as well as spiders and scorpions.

At the end of the Ordovician, however, a dramatic change in Earth's climate resulted in the second most devastating extinction event known to science. An estimated 85 percent of the world's species were lost forever.

Ordovician-Silurian extinction — 444 million years ago

It is believed that, when the North American Appalachian Mountains were first pushed up by plate tectonics,[5] newly exposed silicate rock absorbed massive amounts of carbon dioxide from the atmosphere. The result was a significant cooling of the planet and a relatively short, but severe, ice age. As ice built up at the poles, sea levels dropped by hundreds of feet. Then, as sea levels rose again, ocean oxygen levels declined. This, in turn, caused the oceans to more readily retain dissolved toxins.[6] Sea life, which was almost all life on Earth at that time, was devastated.

Though the vast majority of species that had lived before the Silurian period (444 to 419 million years ago) would be gone forever, over the next 65 million years—through the Silurian and the Devonian geological periods—life once again flourished and diversified. Its migration onto land resumed and accelerated.

Some of the first plants to appear on land were creeping moss-like plants that would send up very small shoots that bifurcated only once or twice. Leaves clung to the shoots like scales. There is nothing quite like them today. Many of these early plants are believed to have migrated from fresh water lakes and rivers where both plants and animals had previously migrated from the sea.[7]

Over the next 20 million years, plants spread inland and diversified to include numerous species of small shrubs. It was only then that animals began to come ashore in significant numbers.

Once the landward migration of vascular plants had begun, each step along the way led to new opportunities. As plant life covered the land, animals that could feed on the vegetation eventually followed. Then, as plants and animals lived and died, their decomposed carcasses created humus to further enrich the soil, leading to even more varieties of plant life and, in turn, providing more opportunities for exploitation by a greater variety of animals.

The lineages of several animal phyla were able to make the transition from sea to land. The Arthropoda lineage would produce mites, millipedes, centipedes, scorpions, spiders, and eventually insects; the Annelida lineage would produce earthworms; the Nematoda lineage would produce roundworms and threadworms; and the Chordata lineage would produce all of the vertebrates— amphibians, reptiles, dinosaurs, birds, and mammals (including us, of course). Interestingly, genetic similarities among all terrestrial vertebrates suggest the Chordata transition to land occurred only once, as a single lineage of fish evolved into the first amphibian tetrapod some 380 to 360 million years ago.

The Devonian period (419 to 359 million years ago) is often called the *"Age of Fishes"* because of the abundant, diverse, and sometimes bizarre fishes that swam the seas. For example, fierce predatory fishes of the genus *Dunkleosteus* grew to as long as 10 meters (30 feet), sported thick armor, and ruled subtropical seas. Instead of teeth, these strange creatures had long bony blades with which they would crush their prey.

Early in the Devonian, forests of ferns and other spore-bearing trees emerged on two supercontinents—Euramerica and Gondwana. The first (wingless) insects appeared. Coiled shell-bearing ammonites appeared in the sea alongside the bottom-feeding trilobites. Life was diverse and abundant, particularly in the sea, and tetrapods were just beginning to move ashore when disaster struck once again.

Late Devonian extinction — 380-360 million years ago

Several times during the Devonian, oxygen levels in the sea dropped significantly, impacting conodonts and the ancient shelled relatives of octopuses and squid called goniatites, among other organisms. The worst of these events, however, was around 372 million years ago. "As oxygen levels plummeted, many reef-building creatures died out, including a major group of sea sponges called the stromatoporoids."[8]

It is not known what caused these events, but volcanism has been hypothesized. A couple of million years before, a volcano in what is now Siberia spewed 240,000 cubic miles of lava. Such an eruption would also have spewed a significant amount of sulfur dioxide into the atmosphere, resulting in a high volume of acid rain. The impact of an asteroid may have contributed, given that one of Earth's largest known impact craters was created about 377 million years ago in what is now Sweden. It also has been suggested that the spread of vascular plants loosened rocky ground, allowing toxic minerals to be washed into streams, rivers, and, ultimately, the sea. Whatever the causes, over a period of some 20 million years at the end of the Devonian, about 75 percent of Earth's species perished.

While life has been vulnerable, it has also been persistent, as it would once again rebound and diversify. After the Devonian came the Carboniferous period (360 to 286 million years ago), so named because it was marked by an abundance of great swampy forests— areas that would eventually turn into the coal deposits humans have used for fuel. (Coal is the high-density remains of ancient trees and other organic material that were partially preserved as they fell into the boggy, oxygen-deprived soils of forest floors.)

With giant trees and a humid atmosphere, these forests resembled today's tropical rain forests, but there were some significant differences. For example, there was little variety in color, since flowering plants had not yet evolved. And there were no sounds of the vocalizations of mammals or the songs of birds. Paleontologist Richard Fortey has called them the "silent forests."[9]

In addition to giant club moss trees and a plethora of ferns, the moist, oxygen-rich atmosphere of these forests produced some rather large amphibians, insects, and other arthropods. Dragonflies were as big as hawks (the largest insects ever known), and there were plant-eating amphibians that grew to lengths of twenty feet. There were six-foot millipedes; Just imagine stepping across one of those fellows, or encountering one of the giant scorpions that were there. Cockroaches were there too, of course—about twice the size of those we see today.

The Carboniferous forests contained an enormous variety of amphibian species, including some that roughly resembled today's alligators and another group that resembled snakes. Amphibians filled the ecological niches of predators and herbivores we usually associate with faster or more cunning reptilian or mammalian species. Since reptiles and mammals had not yet evolved to compete with them, amphibians were able to prosper by freely exploiting the available resources. As a result of this great diversity and abundance of amphibians, the Carboniferous period is often described as the *"Age of Amphibians."*[10]

Permian-Triassic (P-T) extinction — 251 million years ago (The worst of all)

As has happened repeatedly throughout history, it was a change in Earth's climate that brought about a change in its inhabitants during the Permian period (299 to 251 million years ago). Colder and drier weather brought an end to the Carboniferous forests and, with it, an end to the reign of amphibians among vertebrates. With their scaly skin and shelled eggs that were incubated on dry land, reptiles were better suited to the new climate and they began to spread and diversify. New reptilian species evolved to exploit ecological niches that had previously been occupied by amphibians.

The entire Permian period, however, witnessed a gradual decline of life all around the globe. Then, at its end, a series of occurrences caused the most severe mass extinction Earth has ever experienced, sometimes called "the great dying." The precise course of events is not fully understood, but compelling evidence indicates that volcanic activity and a large meteor strike conspired to produce toxic acid rain and dramatic global temperature changes.

In an area known as the Siberian Traps, a series of volcanic eruptions produced more than 720,000 cubic miles of lava. As this occurred, at least 14.5 trillion tons of carbon dioxide, along with methane and other gases, were released into the atmosphere.[11] Near the same time, an enormous asteroid struck what is now Australia.[12] Initially, both events produced massive clouds of smoke and ash, blocking sunlight around the globe for months. This caused a rapid cooling of the planet.

As ice built up at the poles, sea levels dropped significantly and acid snow and rain fell around the world. Then, when the clouds of smoke and ash eventually cleared, massive amounts of greenhouse gases (carbon dioxide, methane, and others) remained in the atmosphere, providing a rapidly warming greenhouse effect. The toxins left by the acid rain along with elevated water temperatures resulted in oxygen depletion in the oceans, leaving most animals unable to breathe. Other factors may have played a role, but rapid (in a million years or so) climate change is pretty well understood to have been the primary culprit.

Sea life was most affected. After having survived for more than 260 million years, the trilobites were lost forever. All the reef corals were destroyed. (The corals alive today are wholly different varieties.) Brachiopods, echinoderms, mollusks, clams, and snails were all decimated. The animals that live today are the progenies of just those few species that survived the extinction event. The vast majority of species of that period met the end of their lineages.

While sea life suffered the most, land-based vertebrates did not escape the carnage. Amphibians had been in decline throughout the Permian, but events near the end of the period also wiped out many of the reptilian species that had only recently taken the place of amphibians. Over about 60,000 years, at the end of the Permian, some 96 percent of sea life and as many as three out of every four species on land perished.[13]

After the "great dying" of the Permian period, life recovered slowly at first. Within a few million years, however, life once again proved resilient. Over the course of the Triassic period (252 to 201 million years ago), new life evolved to fill available niches in the sea and around the globe. A diversity of reef-building creatures prospered and lush ferns and other shrubs and trees covered the landscape.

Modern corals and teleost fishes (the ancestors of tuna, salmon, trout, flounder, catfish, and others) first appeared. Those insects that survived the P-T extinction evolved during the Triassic into the clades from which modern insects would evolve during the Jurassic period and beyond.

Enormous reptiles, such as Plesiosaurs and Ichthyosaurs roamed the seas. The first vertebrates to take flight, Pterosaurs were a group of reptiles that would evolve into hundreds of species, from as small as a sparrow to wingspans of about 5 feet. (The really big ones would not emerge for another 160 million years.)

Both dinosaurs and mammals first appeared during the Triassic, arising from different lineages of the reptiles that dominated the landscape. It was an *"Age of Reptiles."*

Then, disaster struck once again.

Triassic-Jurassic extinction — 201-210 million years ago

At the end of the Triassic, global temperatures rose from 5 to 11 degrees Fahrenheit as a result of the quadrupling of carbon dioxide in the atmosphere. A likely source of the CO_2 and other greenhouse gases was the Central Atlantic Magmatic Province, an enormous area of volcanic activity in central Pangaea, the supercontinent of that time, when all of today's continents were joined together.[14] Today, remnants of those ancient lava flows are found on the four continents surrounding the Atlantic Ocean. This extinction event happened just before Pangaea began to break apart, and appears to have lasted for only about 10,000 years.

The rise in carbon dioxide and the presence of sulfur dioxide once again caused an acidification of the oceans, making it more difficult for sea creatures to make their shells of calcium carbonate. Rising temperatures also resulted in the aridification of much of the land, destroying habitats. All of the possible contributing causes of this massive extinction are not well understood. What is known, however, is that as much as 80 percent of both terrestrial and marine species suddenly died.

When conditions improved, the Jurassic and Cretaceous periods saw a great proliferation of dinosaur species, both carnivores and herbivores, and from tiny to massive. Perhaps the favorite among many young dinosaur enthusiasts was the *Tyrannosaurus rex*. As one of the largest—over 40 feet long and weighing six to seven tons—and one of the fiercest looking terrestrial predators to ever live on Earth, T-rex readily excites the imagination. But there was an abundance of equally fascinating dinosaur species of all sizes and character over those 130 million years.

The first birds emerged from a lineage of theropod dinosaurs. Mammals became common, but remained diminutive—most of them about the size of a mouse for millions of years.

Flying reptiles rebounded, growing more numerous and varied. Some evolved to be very large. By the end of the Cretaceous period, the *Quetzalcoatlus* genus was the largest flying animal of any kind to ever live on Earth, reaching wingspans of as much as 39 feet. Several specimens of these giant flying reptiles have been found in the Big Bend area of West Texas, an area that was near the edge of a sea when those creatures lived.[15]

The Jurassic and Cretaceous periods saw the breakup of the supercontinent Gondwana into roughly the continents we know today. There was a proliferation of flowering plants and new insect species. More modern species of teleost fishes, sharks, sponges, corals, and other sea life also appeared. But, given their great numbers and dominance of the landscape, this time in history is sometimes called the *"Age of Dinosaurs."*

During that time, the level of carbon dioxide in the atmosphere and climatic conditions were very similar to what they are today. But then disaster struck once again. This time, it was the result of an asteroid strike.

Cretaceous-Paleogene extinction – 66 million years ago

In what is now the Caribbean Sea and the Gulf of Mexico, off the coast of the Yucatan Peninsula, an ancient crater from a massive asteroid strike has been found. It has been estimated that it would have taken an asteroid 6 to 9 miles in diameter to have created the 120-mile-wide crater. Such an impact would have punched a hole deep enough to pierce Earth's mantle and send shock waves across the planet, causing volcanic eruptions and earthquakes. Huge volumes of dust, smoke, and sulfuric acid were launched into the atmosphere, since the area of the strike was rich in hydrocarbons and sulfur. It is likely that vegetation within 900 miles of the impact was ignited and a massive tsunami travelled for thousands of miles, destroying sea life and coastal regions.

As a cloud of smoke and debris circled the globe over the following months, photosynthesis was inhibited and ecosystems around the world that support life were severely compromised. The blocking of sunlight for perhaps as long as a year caused a rapid drop in temperatures to below freezing around the globe for an extended period.

Then, after the dust had settled, the effects of acid rain remained in the sea, causing the extinction of plants, phytoplankton, and some corals. Large amounts of greenhouse gases remained in the atmosphere and, as a result, induced a rapid warming. Some scientists believe that volcanic eruptions in what is now India may have exacerbated a lethal global warming.

Today, strata around the world provide clear evidence of this so-called K-T* extinction event 66 million years ago—evidence seen in the mass extinctions of species, as well as a relatively thin layer of the event's debris that fell from the atmosphere around the

---

* "K-T" refers to the boundary between the Cretaceous and Tertiary geological periods. The "K" comes from the German rendition of the word Cretaceous. In 2008, the Tertiary period was officially divided into two— the Paleogene and Neogene periods. (See the Time Scale on page 31.)

globe. An estimated 76 percent of the world's species, including all non-avian dinosaurs and those amazing flying reptiles, were lost.

After Earth had recovered from the K-T event and the dinosaurs were out of the way, the next three geological periods, over a span of 66 million years, would prove to be the *"Age of Mammals"*—the age that would eventually lead to the evolution of humans.

The three most recent geologic periods—the Paleogene, Neogene, and Quaternary—comprise the Cenozoic Era, meaning "modern life." These last 66 million years of the history of life have seen a dramatic evolution of plants and animals around the world while the continents moved into the positions we see today.

The Cenozoic began with a warm and wet (tropical) climate and then became generally cooler and drier over the rest of the era. Many of the more modern plants appeared early. After about 100 million years of diminutive stature, mammals began to grow in size and variety.

An early example was the Coryphodon, a genus of herbivorous mammal with a very small brain and stout body. Since the dinosaurs and larger reptiles had gone, Coryphodons were the largest animals around, at a little over three feet tall and about seven feet long.

Then, about 55 million years ago, the first grasses appeared, enabling the evolution of grazing animals, such as horses and rhinoceroses. (The first known horses were about the size of a small dog, but soon speciated into a diversity of species—almost all of which are now extinct.) Other grazing animals would follow, like camels, moose, deer, and elephants—and in the marsupial world, kangaroos. Today, grasses cover about 20 percent of Earth's land masses.

By the end of the Paleogene period, cooling had created the polar icecaps and flowering plants branched out from ancestors that had survived the K-T extinction event. The speciation of plants and animals accelerated, especially mammals. Mammals branched into a wide diversity of orders and species and, like amphibians, reptiles, and dinosaurs before them, came to utilize and dominate most ecological niches around the world.

One of those orders—Primates—had arisen some 55 to 85 million years ago. Over the course of the Cenozoic Era, it diversified into numerous evolutionary tracks. One of those tracks led to the Hominidae family and to the *Homo* genus and to a series of species that eventually led to us—*Homo sapiens*.

Of course, the evolutionary history of modern human beings is not nearly so simple. It would take an entire book to do justice to that subject. The point here is that we, like the multitudes of organisms that lived and died before us, are the product of an environment in which our life is viable. All of the many extinct species that came before us met their demise as a result of newly untenable environments, whether changes in physical conditions or available resources as a result of new competition from other species or other factors.

In addition to the five mass extinction events described above, a multitude of smaller extinctions have occurred. Some were worldwide, but most were regional or local, as a result of ecological changes. This could have been a change in local geology or climate, or it could be the result of disease or another natural disaster. Each time, some species died while others lived on to propagate their lineages. In fact, more than 99.99 percent of the species that have lived on Earth are now extinct.

Life is vulnerable. Each species thrives only within the narrow ecological parameters in which that species arose. We need look no further than every other planet humankind has discovered to recognize how only the very specific conditions found on Earth are able to sustain life—a uniquely balanced set of conditions that can all too easily be undone.

Consequently, most of the species living today are relatively young, having emerged in only the last few hundred thousand years. In the case of anatomically modern *Homo sapiens*, it is about 200,000 years. All of those ancestral species and cousins that preceded us perished because they were ill-equipped for survival within the environment in which they resided. Although, chances are high that we had a hand in the demise of at least a couple of the other human species who lived contemporaneously with *Homo sapiens.*

The diminutive human species *Homo floresiensis* appears to have had a thriving community on the Indonesian island of Flores until about 50,000 years ago, probably not coincidentally, around the same time *Homo sapiens* arrived on the island.[16] We know *Homo sapiens* interacted with *Homo neanderthalensis* (Neanderthals) because of the recent discovery that many people of European and Asian descent have the remnants of Neanderthal DNA in their genomes. (This indicates interbreeding and a relatedness that was close enough to produce fertile offspring.[17]) Neanderthals lived across Europe and into Central Asia until about 37,000 years ago.

Many modern Southeast Asians also have DNA from the species, or subspecies, called Denisovans—*Homo denisova* or *Homo sapiens denisova*, pending a consensus of their taxonomic status—a population of archaic humans that may have lived as recently as 15,000 years ago. Denisovan DNA is found to be most prevalent in Melanesians, Papuans, and Aboriginal Australians.

We have outlived our *Homo* ancestors and cousins, surviving through numerous environmental challenges, including an Ice Age, because we are clever and resourceful. So clever, in fact, that we learned how to make more effective weapons to hunt and kill game, and how to more effectively use fire to cook food, keep warm, socialize, and to protect ourselves from predators. (Although, other human species also are known to have used fire, hand axes, and bone or stone-tipped spears.[18]) We constructed shelters and made shoes and clothing to protect ourselves from the elements.

Most significantly, about 10,000 to 12,000 years ago we learned how to cultivate and manipulate food crops and how to domesticate livestock. As procuring food became much easier, we could divide our labor and broaden our activities. With the use of language and social interaction, we have continually learned more and improved our standard of living. Naturally, our great success as a species has facilitated population growth.

Over these last 10,000 years, we have been so successful that our numbers and our activity have grown to a point of dramatically affecting the chemistry and character of our planet, just as cyano-bacteria did so many millions of years ago. We have altered many of Earth's natural ecosystems upon which we depend.

Most troubling is that we are living in the midst of Earth's sixth mass extinction event. This time, the extinction is not a result of spewing volcanoes or an asteroid strike. Instead, species are disappearing at a faster rate than at any time in the last 65 million years as a result of expanding human development and consumption. It is becoming increasingly apparent that our own wellbeing is also being put at risk.

The last 11,650 years (following the last major glacial retreat) have traditionally been called the Holocene geological epoch, meaning "entirely new" or "present day." As the effects of human activity on the character of our planet during this time, particularly over the last 200 years, or even the last 70 years, have become more and more apparent, many scientists have concluded that we should adopt Paul Crutzen's recommendation and mark the beginning of a new geological time period—the Anthropocene epoch, "*The Age of Man.*" Most remarkably, we are living in an age in which we can, if we will, control our own destiny.

I do not write this chapter to suggest *Homo sapiens* are in danger of extinction anytime soon, as some do. That would be an underestimation of human ingenuity. I merely seek to point out that, like every other organism that has lived on Earth, we are the product of rather specific ecological parameters, and those parameters are the ones in which we can most viably prosper. Just as importantly, a world most like the one from which we arose is a world in which we can most readily find beauty, wonder, and inspiration, as well as sustenance.

GEOLOGICAL TIME SCALE

Units of Geological Time Scale				Development of Plants and Animals
Eon	Era	Period	Epoch	
Phanerozoic	Cenozoic	Quaternary	Holocene — 0.01	Earliest *Homo sapiens*
			Pleistocene — 1.6	
		Tertiary / Neogene	Pliocene — 5.3	Earliest Hominids
			Miocene — 23.8	
		Tertiary / Paleogene	Oligocene — 33.7	"Age of Mammals"
			Eocene — 55	
			Paleocene — 66	Extinction of dinosaurs and many other species
	Mesozoic	Cretaceous — 145	"Age of Dinosaurs"	First flowering plants
		Jurassic — 208	"Age of Reptiles"	First birds; first mammals
		Triassic — 248		Dinosaurs dominant
	Paleozoic	Permian — 286		Extinction of trilobites and many other marine species
		Carboniferous / Pennsylvanian — 320	"Age of Amphibians"	First reptiles / Large coal swamps
		Carboniferous / Mississippian — 360		Amphibians abundant
		Devonian — 410	"Age of Fishes"	First amphibians / First insects
		Silurian — 444		Fishes dominant
		Ordovician — 490	"Age of Trilobites"	First land plants / First fishes
		Cambrian — 541		First organisms with shells
Proterozoic		Ediacaran — 635	Soft-bodied faunas	
				First multi-celled organisms
			Collectively called Precambrian	Eukaryotic cells
Archean	2500		Comprises about 88% of the geological time scale	Cyanobacteria / Life begins
Hadean	4000			Oldest rocks
	4600 mya			Formation of the Earth

Numbers are mya (millions of years ago)

2

The Anthropocene Epoch

H umankind has accomplished a great many wonderful things over the past 10,000 years. Before then, we *Homo sapiens*, like other human species, had already learned how to make and control fire; how to craft and use stone tools; how to work in teams to hunt with stone or bone tipped spears; and how to cook our food. But over the last 10,000 years, our knowledge and our way of life have changed dramatically. We have learned how to control our own environment and to prosper like no other species on Earth.

We have learned how to cultivate and manipulate food crops in ways that greatly increase their yields. We have domesticated animals for food, for work, for sport, and for companionship.[1] We have invented metallurgy, public sanitation, toilet paper, and the wheel. We learned to write, do mathematics, established cities, formed governments, and invented the printing press.

More recently, we have dammed rivers to make hydro-electricity, built an extensive network of roads and highways, and dug subway tunnels that span long reaches under cities and under the sea. We invented trains, automobiles, electric lights, telephones, radio, television, and airplanes. We invented weather satellites and communication satellites that reach around the world. We have even travelled to the moon and explored our solar system and beyond.

These explorations, discoveries, inventions and innovations, among many others, have resulted in modern amenities that have made life much easier and more productive and rewarding for most of us. They have also enabled us to provide for larger families. Less demanding working conditions, modern medicine, and better nutrition have reduced mortality from diseases and extended life-expectancy, adding to our numbers.

Growing populations have facilitated growing economies and more opportunities for more people to prosper. Population growth, of course, results in greater demand for products and services; and a greater demand for products and services results in greater demand for labor, as well as for innovation and better products and services.

Naturally, as the world population has grown, consumption and industrial activity have increasingly affected the chemistry and character of our planet. Accordingly, we are coming to recognize we are living in a geological epoch that can be defined by human activity. When that epoch precisely began, however, is a subject of some debate.

A few scientists propose that we simply change the name of the Holocene epoch, while most believe the start of the epoch should be delineated by a time when more concrete changes to the planet can be attributed to human activity—a point in time when changes in the chemistry and geology of Earth can be clearly detected and identified in geologic strata, like other geological time designations.

Some would have the start date at 1945, when the first atomic bomb was detonated, or 1963, when the Test Ban Treaty was enacted, because of the worldwide detectability of radioactive fallout resulting from the above-ground atomic bomb tests that occurred between those dates.

Others suggest the detectability of fertilizers, plastics, and fossil fuel remnants would be a more appropriate starting point. Geology Professor Jan Zalasiewicz of the University of Leicester noted that, "We are spoiled for choices. There's a whole array of potential signals out there." For example, man-made microplastics "are now components of sediment around the world, both on land and in the sea."[2] Of course, measurable effects of human activity on our planet occurred long before the atomic bomb tests or even the widespread use of fertilizers, fossil fuels, and plastics.

For a better perspective on how humanity has altered the natural state of our planet, it may be useful for us to be reminded of the history of human development, along with the associated trajectory of human population growth.

At the end of Earth's last major ice age, some 11,650 years ago, began the Holocene geological epoch. There were about four million people in the world at that time,[3] living as nomadic hunter-gatherers, often travelling great distances in search of more abundant game and edible plants. Small groups had already migrated across much of the globe. The two continents of the Western Hemisphere had been discovered and colonized by way of the Bering Strait only within the previous one to two thousand years.

Then, after having lived as hunter-gatherers for nearly 200,000 years (including through a major ice age), the lives of *Homo sapiens* took a dramatic turn. About 10,000 years ago, a few small areas of Southwest Asia and the Eastern Mediterranean saw the domestication of livestock and land cultivation. By 8,000 years ago, domestic agriculture had expanded into more arid areas of Eurasia and North Africa, and it had begun independently in other parts of the world, including the Western Hemisphere. By 4,000 years ago, agricultural activity had spread throughout much of the world.[4]

Along with cultivated crops came permanent villages and societies—civilization. Cultivated crops also brought divisions of labor. Instead of all members of society having to expend a lot of time and energy hunting or gathering, an abundance of food enabled the pursuit of other ways of making life more efficient and rewarding. People could be teachers, potters, carpenters, or metalsmiths.

The first cities were built around 6,000 years ago by Sumerians in what came to be called the Fertile Crescent—the Tigris and Euphrates river valleys of Mesopotamia (modern day Iraq and parts of Kuwait, Iran, Syria, and Turkey)—often referred to as the "Cradle of Civilization." It was there that many important technologies were invented, such as agricultural irrigation, plows, piped water, public sewage, metallurgy (mainly copper), glassmaking, textile weaving, sailboats, the first written language, the first legal code, and the first positional number system. It was also there that the first standing army of professional soldiers was formed.[5]

Perhaps the most consequential of Mesopotamia's inventions was the wheel, around 5,500 years ago. It probably began as a potter's wheel before being used for transportation on wheelbarrows, carts, and then chariots and wagons. Perhaps the first mechanical invention, the wheel and axle assembly dramatically enhanced human productivity and mobility.

Soon thereafter, the great pyramids were built in Egypt and cities grew larger and more numerous around much of the world. Encyclopedia Britannica has called the years from 5,000 to 2,500 years ago "the urban revolution," as more and more people filled cities. By 5,000 years ago, the world population had grown to about 14 million people.

Ultimately, it was the construction of great cities and extensive roadways, along with large-scale agricultural production, that most significantly affected the landscape. A recent collaborative study conducted by 255 archaeologists from around the world, called the ArchaeoGLOBE Project, has shown that, by 3,000 years ago, the clearing of forests and invasive farming practices had resulted in significant alterations of terrains around the globe. A lead author of the study, Andrea Kay of the Max Planck Institute for Science of Human History in Jena, Germany, explained, "While modern rates and scales of anthropogenic global change are far greater than those of the deep past, the long-term cumulative changes wrought by early food producers are greater than many realize."[6]

By 3,000 years ago, the world population had grown to about 50 million people,[7] and human-induced species extinctions and deforestation were well underway—though perhaps not significantly enough to constitute a permanent change in the character of the planet. In the absence of human intervention, nature has a remarkable capacity to reclaim its territory in just a few centuries.

Bronze and iron came into use, and advances were made in architectural construction, ship building, dikes, dams, irrigation, and other agricultural techniques. The Greeks built impressive structures, along with the foundations of Western philosophy. The Romans built an elaborate system of aqueducts for water transport, architectural marvels like the Forum, the Pantheon, and the Colosseum, and plenty of roads throughout their empire. The Chinese built a Great Wall and a remarkable Terracotta Army. There were innovations in the manipulation of iron and other metals for uses in tools, architectural construction, and weapons. By 2,020 years ago—1 CE—the population had grown to about 250 to 300 million people.

Intellectual and technological advances were made all along the way. The Indians invented buttons and the concept of zero in mathematics. The Persians invented the idea of human rights, the first monotheistic religion, and algebra. The Chinese invented silk, paper (then toilet paper), gunpowder, fireworks, the first gun (made of bamboo) and the first compass. With advances in the design and construction of ships, explorers and migrants began to travel the world, particularly after Europeans discovered the spherical character of the planet and the Western Hemisphere. Cities, agricultural tracts, and human populations continued to grow at increasing rates. By 500 years ago, the world population had reached about 450 million people.

With the European discovery of the Western Hemisphere, begin-ning with Christopher Columbus' 1492 landing in what is now the Bahamas, came a great transfer of plants, animals, and peoples between the continents of Europe and the Americas. It marked the beginning of what we now call "globalization."

The *Equus* genus originated when the continents of North America and Europe were connected, but after their separation North American horses went extinct about 10,000 to 12,000 years ago. Columbus introduced Spanish horses to the continent on his second voyage in 1493. More Spanish horses came with explorers and settlers. Only then, could some of the Native American tribes become horse cultures over the subsequent three hundred years.

In addition to horses, Europeans brought cattle, pigs, sheep, domestic goats, chickens, wheat, rice, barley, oats, and fruit crops. Conversely, a great many "New World" staple crops were introduced to Europe. Those included maize (corn), potatoes, sweet potatoes, green beans, squash, tomatoes, bananas, avocados, pineapple, peppers, maple syrup, sunflowers, chocolate, and tobacco. Domestic turkeys also originated in the New World.[8] The exchange of these agricultural commodities and other plants and animals, as well as the exchange of communicable diseases (mostly from Europe to the Americas) has been called the "Columbian Exchange."

Estimates of the pre-Columbian populations of the hundreds of thriving tribes and societies of the Western Hemisphere vary. By some estimates, they totaled about one-third of the world popu-lation. But they were decimated by contact with Europeans, through conquest, enslavement, and especially diseases like smallpox and measles. (Sometimes disease was intentionally spread among in-digenous peoples by giving them blankets that had been used by smallpox patients.) Historians estimate that, by 1650, the number of indigenous people in North and South America had been reduced by 90 to 95 percent as a result of European conquest.

Similar exchanges of biological organisms, including people, took place between all the inhabited continents of the world as land

and sea travel became more prevalent between Europe, Asia, Africa, Australia, New Zealand, and North and South America.

Coffee, for example, came from Africa. So did okra, yams, black-eyed peas, millets, sorghum, sesame, malaria, yellow fever, and, of course, slaves.

In a forward to the re-publication of Alfred W. Crosby, Jr.'s classic book, *The Columbian Exchange*, J.R. McNeill noted, "It is well to remember that before 1880 most of the people who crossed the Atlantic to the Americas were Africans, and before 1820 four out of every five transatlantic migrants hailed from Africa."[9] According to the U.S. Library of Congress, over a period of 300 years, an estimated 15 to 20 million Africans were brought to the Americas as slaves. "Of those, a little more than 400,000 were sent to the 13 British colonies and, later, the United States."[10]

As travel expanded throughout the world, rats and other pests came along as stowaways to places they had never before been, and where they enjoyed an absence of natural predators. With no predators to reduce their numbers, rats can easily proliferate and ravage ecosystems.

Native to Southeast Asia, Pacific rats called "kiore" immigrated along with Polynesian seafarers to places like Hawaii, Fiji, Tonga, Samoa, and New Zealand. "A recent study of pollen and animal remains on Easter Island concluded that it wasn't humans who deforested the landscape; rather, it was the rats that came along for the ride and then bred unchecked. The native palms couldn't produce seeds fast enough to keep up with their appetites."[11]

The islands of New Zealand have no native terrestrial mammals. The only indigenous mammals there are bats and marine mammals like seals, dolphins, and whales. When Maori settlers brought kiore rats to the island a little more than 700 years ago, the rats soon wiped out a number of local species. Then, the kiore were decimated when European settlers brought the more aggressive Norway rats. (Of course, everywhere Europeans have gone, so have their rats.) Because of the continuing destructive nature of these animals, along with stoats (a kind of weasel) and Australian possums, New Zealand has now committed itself to eradicating all predatorial mammals, save a few inside domestic cats, by 2050.[12]

Modern bridges and tunnels have connected land masses that had previously been divided by the sea, and the Panama and Suez canals have joined together previously separated oceans— further diluting and dispersing the world's biodiversity.

Population growth and increasingly easy world travel have continued to facilitate the exchange of plants, animals, peoples, and diseases all over the world—thereby significantly changing its character, sometimes for the better, but often to its detriment.

Not long after the invention of the steam engine, the "Industrial Revolution" began around 1760 and lasted until about 1830. Those years saw a great expansion of mechanical manufacturing and mass production. The iron and steel industries flourished. With modern production methods, textiles became a significant part of the economies of Europe and the United States.

The Industrial Revolution also began a dramatic increase in the burning of coal, as it was used to heat water for the steam engines of trains, ships, and factory machinery. Vast amounts of coal were burned in blast furnaces for working iron and steel, as well as for cooking and for heating homes. By the beginning of the 19th century, the burning of coal and deforestation grew to levels that began to significantly increase the amount of carbon dioxide in the atmosphere.

The world prospered and, in the Western World in particular, the standard of living for most people was on the rise. In merely 300 years, from 1500 to 1800, the world population more than doubled, reaching nearly one billion people.

A "Second Industrial Revolution" is said to have begun in the late 19th century, lasting until the beginning of World War I. During that time great advances were made in technology and massive infrastructure projects were undertaken. Telegraph systems accompanied an increasingly complex network of railways. Public water, natural gas, and sewer systems were more widely installed. The electric light bulb was invented and the electrification of public streets, industry, and homes began. Both electric motors and gasoline-fueled engines were being improved and more widely used. Refined oil was replacing coal on several fronts, and the chemicals industry began to take hold. By 1900, the world population had reached 1.65 billion people.

Between the 20th century's two World Wars, the Great Depression engulfed the world. In the United States, efforts to end the Depression involved massive government spending, both to put people to work and to modernize the nation. Numerous large-scale infrastructure projects were undertaken. LaGuardia Airport, the Lincoln Tunnel, the Triborough Bridge, the Hoover Dam, the Bixby Bridge, the San Antonio River Walk, and many other assets were constructed with public funding.

In 1932, only 10 percent of rural America had electricity.[13] The Rural Electrification Administration built hydroelectric dams and brought electricity and productivity to American farms. The public works initiatives were then interrupted by World War II. Ultimately, it was the massive government spending for the war that brought an end to the Great Depression.

Throughout human history, it has been military initiatives that most forcefully drive innovation and technological advances. By the end of World War II, great strides had been made in engineering, especially naval and aircraft engineering. Jet engines were invented, rocket engines were improved, and the atom was split. In addition to making powerful bombs, scientists and engineers soon learned how to harness nuclear energy for generating electricity and the propulsion of surface ships and submarines.

Despite having lost as many as 80 million people in the war, by 1950, the world population had reached 2.5 billion people. Then, in only the next 70 years, that number would grow more than three-fold, to 7.8 billion people by 2020.

After World War II, a "baby boom" was accompanied by unprecedented economic growth and prosperity in much of the world. Sometimes referred to as the "Great Acceleration," it was a time of dramatically accelerating population growth, technological development, and globalization. In the United States, it began with what we like to remember as the "Norman Rockwell years"—a time of great optimism and rising standards of living.

Seven decades later, that promise has held true for much of the world. Most people have plenty of food,* indoor plumbing, electricity, and access to modern medical care.

Most remarkably, the "human condition"—how we live and, ultimately, who we are as *Homo sapiens*—has been completely transformed over these past 10,000 years. The advent of agriculture and the resulting divisions of labor began a cascade of developments that have brought us to the modern age in which we live.

As the cumulative knowledge of our ancestors has been passed down from innumerable generations through languages and cultures, we have come from small groups of "hunter-gatherers" with little more than sticks, stones, and fire for tools, to complex societies all over the globe and an interconnected global community. Today, our personal possessions and conveniences are almost exclusively the products of the labor and ideas of other people—people from all over the world and ideas throughout human history.

---

* This description is not intended to discount the famines that people have experienced in some parts of the world, or the ongoing lack of adequate nutrition among poor people in all societies today. It is, instead, a generalization of human development and food production. (There is more about food production and distribution in Chapter 3.)

With advances in medicine, we have largely transcended the forces of evolutionary natural selection. Eyeglasses and contact lenses enable the visually impaired to see. Hearing aids and cochlear implants enable people to hear. Artificial limbs enable function and mobility. Lives are regularly saved with pacemakers, artificial valves, and transplanted hearts. We can aid fertility and perform cesarean sect-ions. We can cure diseases and we can repair or transplant failing kidneys, livers, lungs, and other components of the human body.

Many of us have a remarkably high standard of living. In the developed world, we have two or three-car households, often with garages to match, in single-family homes. We have flat-screen televisions, desktop computers, iPads, cell phones, and an extensive array of appliances and gadgets for our convenience and entertainment. We can easily travel by car or by airplane. Many of us have the means to readily travel the entire world.

We have a great many modern conveniences, like disposable diapers, K-Cups®, dishware, straws, aluminum foil, and the disposable containers and packaging for food, beverages, and a multitude of consumer products, and we have convenient services that take all that refuse away. There can be little doubt that today is the most fortunate time to be alive in human history.

Our growing numbers, however, are increasingly presenting problems that threaten our way of life. The enormous volume of our consumption and waste is negatively impacting the very same planetary ecosystems from which we arose and within which we have prospered.

Landfills are scarring the landscape and tainting water supplies. Precious metal and coal mining operations also very often contaminate local water sources. Untreated and uncontained sewage and ever-increasing runoff of chemical fertilizers, pesticides, and other pollutants threaten aquifers, reservoirs, lakes, and rivers. Many of the world's most crucial aquifers are being dangerously depleted by agricultural and municipal consumption.

Non-biodegradable plastics are polluting our land and our oceans. According to the U.S. National Oceanic and Atmospheric Administration (NOAA), some 8 million metric tons of plastic enter our oceans each year.[14] Plastics are found in 100 percent of sea turtles and 60 percent of sea birds, as these creatures mistake microplastic particles for food. Fish and other sea life have also been heavily impacted by plastics.

A recent study of sea salt brands across the world found that, of the 39 brands tested, 36 of them (90 percent) contained plastics. (The three brands that did not contain plastic were a refined sea salt from Taiwan, a refined rock salt from China, and an unrefined sea salt produced by solar evaporation from France.)[15]

The burning of fossil fuels and deforestation are resulting in an alarming increase in the amount of carbon dioxide in the atmosphere, the most prevalent of the greenhouse gases that cause global warming. "The annual rate of increase of atmospheric carbon dioxide over the past 60 years is about 100 times faster than previous natural increases."[16] As a result, there is more CO_2 in the atmosphere today than at any time in the last 800,000 years.

The world's forests absorb carbon dioxide. But, according to the U.N. Food and Agriculture Organization, an estimated 18 million acres of forest are destroyed each year by logging and by agricultural and urban expansion. Afghanistan lost 70 percent of its forests in just the two decades prior to 2007. In addition to losing the CO_2-absorbing trees, this has put a great strain on the economic prospects of the country. In Brazil, the destruction of particularly valuable CO_2-absorbing rainforest has surged to a loss of more than 2.7 million acres in just one year, from August 2019 to July 2020.[17]

In addition to emitting carbon dioxide, petrochemical exploration and refinement, as well as agricultural livestock, emit the most potent of the greenhouse gases—methane. Methane is 25 times more powerful at trapping heat in the atmosphere than carbon dioxide. Because of the way the two gases breakdown over time, when measured over a 20-year period, methane is 84 times more potent as a greenhouse gas than CO_2. And 60 percent of the world's methane emissions are a result of human activity.[18]

There are also some 680 million pigs and about 990 million cows alive today. These animals and the processes of their agriculture are producers of carbon dioxide, methane, and nitrous oxide—all potent greenhouse gases. A single cow emits from 30 to 130 gallons of methane each day, mostly from belching, with smaller amounts from flatulence and manure. Of course, an ever-growing human population requires an ever-growing food supply. And in the West in particular, many people prefer a high-protein diet of meats.

A good example of how human ingenuity and ever-increasing human consumption has dramatically changed our world can be seen in the modern chicken. Before the 1950s, chickens were primarily raised on small farms for the purpose of egg production. While some egg farms had grown in scale after the electric incubator was introduced in 1923, chickens were sold for meat only when hens had outlived their egg production or when chicks had hatched out male. Chicken meat was simply not very substantial or desirable, as compared to pork or beef.

That began to change after the USDA* organized the Chicken of Tomorrow contest beginning in 1945 with support from A&P Food Stores and the poultry industry. As enthusiastically described in the *Saturday Evening Post* in 1947, the contest's objective was to breed "one bird chunky enough for the whole family—a chicken with breast meat so thick you can carve it into steaks, with drumsticks that contain a minimum of bones buried in layers of juicy dark meat, all costing less instead of more."[19] Through selective breeding, the contest resulted in the creation of faster-growing, larger and more meaty chickens.

Over the course of the next few decades, selective breeding strategies, along with feed and antibiotic supplement strategies, grew so complex and so effective that they became closely guarded intellectual property. Under strict breeding, feeding, and environ-

---

* United States Department of Agriculture

mental controls, the chickens we eat today grow twice as fast, are more than twice the size, and have five times more body mass than those of the 1940s.[20]

The life span of today's broiler chickens is only six weeks before slaughter, and the birds are so meaty they can hardly stand up on their own. The free-roaming, weather-tolerant breeds that dominated before the 1950s have largely been supplanted by these hefty man-made beasts.

The demands of conscientious consumers who want more humane treatment of all livestock are beginning to reverse the trend of increasingly unnatural chickens. Nevertheless, the enormous markets for chicken meat and eggs are continuing to make an indelible mark on our planet.

Today, there are about 24 billion chickens alive in the world (that is 3.1 for every person on Earth), as some 66 billion are slaughtered each year for consumption. They are the most numerous birds on Earth. (In a distant second place, at 1.5 billion, is the tiny red-billed quelea, often call the feathered locust in its sub-Saharan African home.[21]) The total biomass of domesticated poultry, mostly chickens, has been calculated to be about three times the biomass of all the world's wild bird species combined.[22]

It has been suggested that, given the enormous volume of chicken consumption across the world, discarded chicken bones could provide a marker for paleontologists and geologists of the distant future to discover—arguably the most significant biological remnant of our age. They might even conclude that they have discovered the *"Age of the Chicken."*[23]

It was we humans, however, who created those chickens—chickens so far removed from their natural ancestors[24]—and it is we humans who have grown them in such great numbers in order to feed our own great numbers. There can be no reasonable doubt that we are living in the *Age of Humankind*—living in the midst of the Anthropocene geological epoch.

3

Bring in the Crowd

O ver most of the history of our species, *Homo sapiens*, average life expectancy was about 30 to 35 years. Individuals could live into their sixties, seventies, or longer. But the *average* life expectancy of humans was kept low because of our susceptibility to infectious diseases and a great many other hazards—particularly among younger adults, children, and infants.

In the Bible's book of *Leviticus*, written about 3,000 years ago, God was reported to have instructed Moses on the relative value of human beings. A male between the ages of 20 and 60 years was worth 50 shekels, while a female of that age was worth only 30 shekels; a male between the ages of 5 and 20 years was worth 20 shekels, while a female of that age was worth 10 shekels; a male between the ages of 1 month and 5 years was worth 5 shekels, while a female of that age was worth 3 shekels. There was no value at all assigned to children under the age of 1 month.[1] We might imagine a number of reasons for such valuations, but the lack of any value at all for children under one month of age may have been because of their limited likelihood of survival.

Three thousand years later, little had changed. In the mid-seventeenth century, a British haberdasher-turned-demographer developed the first scientifically valid analysis of mortality rates in London. John Graunt published his findings in 1662, declaring that, "for every hundred Londoners born, thirty-six of them would die before their sixth birthday," and less than half would survive beyond adolescence.[2] In a validation of Mr. Graunt's work, historical demographer Anthony Wrigley conducted a study in the 1970s that concluded, "life expectancy at birth in London during the seventeenth century was just under thirty-five years."[3] It was not until the last couple of centuries that infant and childhood mortality rates began a steady decline. This change has been the result of a growing number of health and safety innovations.

Over the last two centuries, countless lives have been saved by better sanitation systems (including the introduction of the basic toilet), the invention of vaccines, artificial fertilizers, pasteurization, chlorination, refrigeration, antibiotics, insulin, blood transfusions, radiology, pacemakers, kidney dialysis, cesarean sections, and a very long list of other medical discoveries and treatments. More recently, seat belts, airbags, and a multitude of other safety innovations have saved millions more.

Average life expectancy in the developed world today is about 75 to 80 years for men, with an additional 4 to 5 years for women. In the developing world, life expectancy is about 55 to 70 years for men. (Average life expectancy varies around the world, and continues to rise in developing countries as they modernize.)

Of course, as more and more people have been saved from premature death, they have been able to grow up to have their own children. As a result, the last two centuries has seen exponential population growth, as we can see with the chart on page 59.

Naturally, a longer, healthier, and more assured life is of great value to each of us. At the same time, however, our rapidly growing population is increasingly presenting serious challenges to the quality and to the predictability of our and our children's lives.

In his 1968 bestselling book, *The Population Bomb*, Stanford University Professor Paul Ehrlich warned that resource depletion and food shortages resulting from overpopulation could cause massive starvation as early as the 1970s or 80s. Ehrlich supposed that the economic and agricultural productivity of Earth was reaching its natural limit, while population growth was going unchecked. What Ehrlich failed to recognize, however, was the so-called "Green Revolution" that had already been well underway.

The term "Green Revolution" refers to the agricultural pro-ductivity gains resulting from new technologies and practices that were employed in the 1950s and 60s. Of course, it didn't stop there. New innovations are continually being imagined and implemented, and we continue to have plenty of food. This is not to say that everyone has enough food. Food shortages occur often in locales that suffer from drought, war, or inadequate distribution. Even in the United States, some people go hungry while 30 to 40 percent of our food production goes to waste.[4]

In the half century since Ehrlich's book was published, the world's population has doubled, while the number of people living in extreme poverty has fallen from a little more than half to about 10 percent. "In the world's developing countries, undernourishment has dropped from more than 30 percent in 1970 to close to 10 percent today."[5]

Ehrlich might have been well advised to have noted similar predictions that had been made by the English cleric and economist Thomas Robert Malthus in his 1798 work, *An Essay on the Principle of Population*. Of course, Malthus's prediction came before the advent of mechanization and more advanced fertilizing, selective breeding, and irrigation techniques. Malthus's prediction was so dire that he proclaimed that health and prosperity of humanity was dependent upon wars, diseases, and "moral restraint" to keep populations under control.

Recent history and human ingenuity have demonstrated that it is unlikely we have yet reached the limit of feeding a growing population. Nevertheless, it stands to reason there is a limit, and it may be closer than is widely appreciated. In any case, an ability to feed ourselves is not the only measure of a life worth living.

Issues surrounding population growth have been important topics of discussion and political debate for many years. When pharmaceutical birth control was invented in 1953, resistance to its use arose in the Catholic Church and elsewhere, on the grounds of immorality. In 1968, Pope Paul VI banned all contraception for Catholics in the encyclical, "Humanae Vitae." Opposition to birth control has since grown among some Protestants and Mormons in conjunction with their opposition to abortion.

Nevertheless, in the 1960s and 70s in particular, population growth was of grave concern, and efforts to slow it enjoyed political support across most political divides. Unlike today, many of the most vocal proponents of birth control and women's rights were members of the Republican Party.

Arizona Senator Barry Goldwater (a "conservative's conservative") and his wife Peggy were long-time supporters of family planning efforts. With the help of Planned Parenthood founder Margaret Sanger, Peggy Goldwater opened the first birth control clinic in Phoenix in 1937. In those years, to be a conservative Republican meant to believe in limited government, personal freedom, and individual responsibility. This, of course, meant that women were to be trusted with managing their own reproductive health decisions.

In fact, five of the seven Supreme Court justices who signed on to the 1973 Roe v. Wade decision that legalized abortion were Republican appointees. One of them, Harry Blackmun, wrote the decision. (One Democrat and one Republican dissented.)

As a United States congressman from 1967 to 1971, George H.W. Bush was a principal backer of Title X legislation, which allocated federal funds for groups like Planned Parenthood to provide reproductive health services for poor Americans. In a speech on the House floor, Bush proclaimed,

> I see no reason why similar programs of education and family planning assistance—all on a voluntary basis—should not be instituted in the United States on a massive scope. It is imperative that we do so: Not only to fight poverty at its roots, not only to cut down on our welfare

costs, but also to eliminate the needless suffering of unwanted children and overburdened parents.

President Richard Nixon signed the legislation into law in 1970 with overwhelming bi-partisan support. Bush's zealousness on the issue even earned him the light-hearted nickname "Rubbers" from his congressional colleagues.[6]

In 1971, Nixon made Bush ambassador to the United Nations, where he took the effort to the world. As ambassador, Bush promoted the newly established UN Population Fund (UNFPA), writing, "Success in the population field under United Nations leadership, may, in turn, determine whether we can resolve successfully the other great questions of peace, prosperity, and individual rights that face the world."[7]

There was strong bi-partisan support in the United States Congress for these efforts, particularly among Republicans, who saw them as a means to slow the population growth of poor and unstable countries and to empower women, thereby improving their lives. That all changed, however, when Ronald Reagan was elected president.

As governor of California in 1967, Reagan signed a bill that virtually legalized abortion in that state, at the urging of his most conservative advisors.[8] He became appalled, however, when a subsequent surge in abortions was reported. It is unclear whether the surge was actually a significant increase in abortions or it was merely an apparent increase because abortions were no longer illegal and hidden. In any case, Reagan became a vocal and per-suasive opponent of abortion, particularly after the U.S. Supreme Court legalized abortion in 1973 with what many believe to be dubious reasoning and an extrajudicial construct in its ruling. He then brought that stance to the Republican Party when he won the presidency in 1980.

Because many of the most ardent opponents of abortion are also opposed to birth control, the two matters have become conflated. Then, with the mendacious and blunt instruments of political ambition among politicians, organizations that provide access to birth control and abortion, like Planned Parenthood, became the targets of demonization. So, even though making birth control available to poor people reduces the incidence of abortion, support for such efforts has largely fallen away within the Republican Party.

In 1985, the U.S. Congress enacted Kemp-Kasten (an amendment to an appropriations bill), which prohibited U.S. funds from being made available to "any organization or program which, as determined by the president of the United States, supports or participates in the management of a program of coercive abortion or involuntary sterilization." The amendment was enacted after concerns arose about China's population control policies and UNFPA's work in China. The United States and other governments "have found no evidence that UNFPA directly engages in coercive abortion or involuntary sterilization in China, and more generally, UNFPA does not promote abortion as a method of family planning or fund abortion services."[9] Nevertheless, United States support for the UNFPA was withheld during the second term of the Reagan Administration and during the terms of George W. Bush and Donald Trump, despite the United States' crucial role in its creation in 1969. Support was restored during the Clinton, Obama, and Biden Administrations.[10]

The subjects of population control and birth control have become politicized and incorporated into the so-called "culture war," where political battles are waged over individual liberties and varying preferences for cultural norms. As a result of the political challenges, along with the fact that many of the predictions of overpopulation doom have not yet come to pass, the subject of population control is scarcely mentioned in today's United States Congress by either party.

In fact, among highly developed nations, a lack of population growth is of great concern. Birth rates tend to fall in prosperous nations, resulting in a demographic imbalance of the young and the old. A large population of pensioners is difficult to support with a minority of young people. For that reason, China has abandoned its one-child mandate. (China recently announced its endorsement of three-child families.) Demographic imbalances have necessitated a reduction of pension benefits among the wealthy nations of northern Europe. And it has been a strain on the American Social Security system (Though that strain has been somewhat mitigated by a regular influx of legal and even, dare we admit it, illegal immigrants.[11]).

Another reason population control has become less urgent in the minds of many is that the rate of the world's population growth has begun to fall. The Population Division of the United Nations Department of Economic and Social Affairs has projected that by about 2100, the world's population will begin to level off at around 10.9 billion people. That is, today's population of 7.9 billion people will grow by about 38 percent in the next 80 years, with most of that growth in Africa and Asia.[12]

India recently passed China in becoming the most populous country in the world. By the end of this century, Africa will be the most densely populated continent; Islam will be the most common religion; And most of the world's people will be rather old.[13]

So, the questions at hand are: Will we be able to adequately feed some 11 billion people indefinitely? How will the attempt affect our planet? What will be the other effects of such massive human development, consumption, and waste disposal?

A Tale of Two Visions

Born in the United States in 1902, William Vogt could be considered the father of the modern environmental movement. In his 1948 book, *Road to Survival*, Vogt argued that ever increasing human development and consumption was wreaking havoc on Earth's natural ecosystems. Unlike Malthus and Ehrlich, he made no predictions of imminent food shortages. Instead, he expressed concern for what expanding food production was doing to the planet.

Vogt argued that natural ecosystems have limits to how much they can produce, and when those limits are exceeded for extended periods, the ecosystems become irreparably damaged or destroyed. Large scale *unnatural* agricultural production can cause soil exhaustion, erosion, water contamination, water depletion, and then, ultimately, desertification.[14]

Just as Vogt predicted, desertification is currently degrading as much as 12 million hectares (about 30 million acres) of arable land each year. The United Nations Food and Agriculture Organization has estimated that by 2030, Africa will have lost two-thirds of its arable land if the current trend continues.[15]

Furthermore, the extensive use of synthetic chemical fertilizers results in runoff that pollutes adjacent ecosystems and eventually runs into the sea, creating aquatic dead zones. The clearing of forests and woodlands to make way for large agricultural tracts displaces wildlife and induces species extinctions. Large-scale agricultural irrigation can drain aquifers and create water shortages for human populations.[16]

Vogt's central message was that it is in the best interest of humankind to control population growth and to refrain from mass-producing and unnatural agricultural methods. Instead, we should implement more natural and renewable agricultural techniques— crop rotation; smaller and more diverse tracts of plantings; less chemical fertilizers; more use of manure; less use of herbicides and pesticides; and more composting and natural predation—in order to preserve the ecosystems upon which we will always depend.

Born in the United States 12 years after Vogt, Norman Borlaug would become known as the father of the Green Revolution. Borlaug believed that *science* could enable farmers to produce enough food for a growing population, as well as resolve any associated environmental issues.

When Vogt's *Road to Survival* was published, Borlaug was a young plant pathologist working in Mexico for the Rockefeller Foundation. The bulk of the foundation's work there was intended to help Mexico's corn farmers increase their yields. But Borlaug was tasked with a side project aimed at solving the problem of black stem rust, a fungus that has affected wheat ever since its domestication thousands of years ago. Cold weather kills the rust, but since Mexico doesn't experience much cold, the fungus persists and then seasonally blows across the border.[17]

Borlaug, the only Rockefeller researcher working with wheat in the mid-1950s, was able to create a wheat variety that was resistant to many strains of rust. He then bred a "semi-dwarf" wheat that was more resistant to winds. The shorter wheat could ingest larger doses of fertilizer and produce much more robust heads of grain. As a result of Borlaug's work, wheat yields increased by as much as 10-fold, prompting a USAID[*] official to declare a "Green Revolution," thus, establishing the term now associated with the 20th century's great leap forward in agricultural production.[18]

In 1962, the Rockefeller Foundation in association with the Ford Foundation opened the International Rice Research Institute (IRRI) in the Philippines. At that time, much of Asia suffered from poverty and hunger, and communism appeared to some populations to offer a better future. In order to demonstrate the advantages of capitalism, the United States government then supported efforts to modernize rice production.

Using the methods that Norman Borlaug had pioneered, IRRI researchers developed new, high-yield rice varieties. Over the next two or three decades the new varieties took hold across Asia, nearly tripling rice yields. This alleviated hunger and facilitated soaring population growth. As author Charles C. Mann put it, "Seoul and Shanghai, Jaipur and Jakarta; shining skyscrapers, pricey hotels,

---

[*] United States Agency for International Development

traffic-jammed streets ablaze with neon—all were built atop a foundation of laboratory-bred rice."[19]

Of course, research did not end with the 20th century. In addition to the selective breeding techniques employed by Borlaug and many others, genetic engineering is now advancing food production. And in some respects, genetic engineering may help to address at least some of the concerns articulated by William Vogt and environmentalists.

In an effort to reduce the need for nitrogen-rich, polluting synthetic fertilizers and abundant amounts of water, researchers are looking for ways to enable plants to perform comparably without them. Largely funded by the Bill and Linda Gates Foundation, the C4 Rice Consortium, consisting of seven institutions in five countries,[20] is engaged in just such an effort—an ambitious endeavor that, if successful, could usher in a new Green Revolution.

The genetic engineering of plants typically involves placing genetic material from one organism into another. One of the best-known examples is Monsanto's Roundup Ready soybean, which contains a bit of DNA from a particular bacterium found in a Louisiana waste pond, where it was seen to survive exposure to glyphosate (the active ingredient in Roundup). Fields of the altered plants can be sprayed with Roundup herbicide to kill weeds without harming the soybeans. Apart from a tasteless and non-toxic protein, the Roundup Ready soybeans are practically identical to other soybeans.

The C4 Rice Consortium, on the other hand, is attempting to do something much more complicated and revolutionary—change the very process of photosynthesis in rice plants. "C4" refers to a four-carbon intermediate molecule used in the process of photo-synthesis in some fast-growing plants, such as corn, sugar cane, daisies, and cabbage. (About three percent of all plants use the C4 process.) These plants require less fertilizer and less water than other plants. Rice is a C3 plant and researchers are trying to find a way to convert it into a C4 plant. If successful, its photosynthetic efficiency is predicted to increase by half, while using half as much water and much less fertilizer.[21]

Theoretically, the C4 approach could be applied to other food crops, helping to ensure an abundant food supply despite a growing population and dwindling resources of water and land. And a reduction in the use of synthetic chemical fertilizers could help to preserve crucial ecosystems.

In his illuminating 2018 book, *The Wizard and The Prophet*, author Charles C. Mann described the work of William Vogt and Norman Borlaug as competing visions that have become entrenched in rigid ideologies—one of constraint and conservation, and one of innovation and progress.

As is common with ideologies, their adherents often fail to recognize the merits of competing or alternative views, making the integration of views and methods more difficult. But, as we can plainly see, innovation will be needed to feed 11 billion people—or even the current 7.9 billion people for an extended period. Just as crucially, we will need to stop the degradation of Earth's ecosystems if we intend to retain a habitable planet.

There is little doubt that human ingenuity can make the necessary advances to feed a great deal more people. But, regardless of whether or not we are able to produce enough food for the coming 11 billion people, our natural world is already disappearing at an unsustainable rate.

Diminishing resources, such as fishery stocks, fertile land, fresh water, precious metals, and oil, are resulting in conflicts among nations. The U.S. Central Intelligence Agency, the United Nations, and the World Bank have repeatedly warned that water shortages resulting from pollution, depletion, and climate change will increasingly lead to armed conflict among nations and regional populations around the world.[22]

China has seized disputed islands in the South China Sea that are claimed by the Philippines, Vietnam, and Indonesia. China is using intimidation with its massive military to claim those areas for fishing, oil extraction, and military operations.

We do well to remember that Nazi Germany's 1941 invasion of the Soviet Union was largely motivated by Hitler's desire to seize the extraordinarily fertile pasturelands of Ukraine, north of the Black Sea. While Germany struggled to have enough food, in Ukraine, "field upon field of cereals stretched across flat plains as far as the eye could see." Hitler envisioned the area would become the breadbasket of his great empire. It was not only territorial conquest that Hitler sought, it also was a quest for food that led to the violent deaths of millions of German soldiers, Russians, and Jews.[23]

As we add another 40 percent to our numbers in the decades ahead, we will be facing increasingly degraded soils, depleted water supplies, and the effects of climate change. It seems highly likely, therefore, that increasing hunger, mass migrations, and conflict will be on the horizon too.

Of course, it is not just the availability of enough food that is of concern. As the world population has grown denser and we have encroached more into wild lands, some communities are living closer to monkeys and apes that are traded as bushmeat and pets. Two strains of HIV virus are thought to have come from chimpanzee bushmeat sold in Central African markets. The Ebola virus may have come from butchering gorilla meat. People are also increasingly coming in contact with cattle, pigs, chickens, and ducks in factory farms. It has been from these contacts that avian and swine flus have recently arisen in humans.

The COVID-19 worldwide pandemic, which is believed to have originated in bats traded at a wildlife market in China, was predicted by scientists for some time before its occurrence.[24] Because of the increasing number of close contacts with exotic wildlife, we can expect pandemics to become more likely in the future, perhaps even common.

As we will see in the following chapter, wildlife numbers are plummeting and species are going extinct at a rate Earth has not experienced in 65 million years. Continuing population growth and ever-expanding human development and consumption will inevitably result in more and more losses of Earth's natural ecosystems.

It seems only prudent, therefore, that we should look for opportunities to encourage slower population growth and to preserve our remaining natural resources. Our way of life may well depend on it. Certainly, our children's will.

World Population Growth

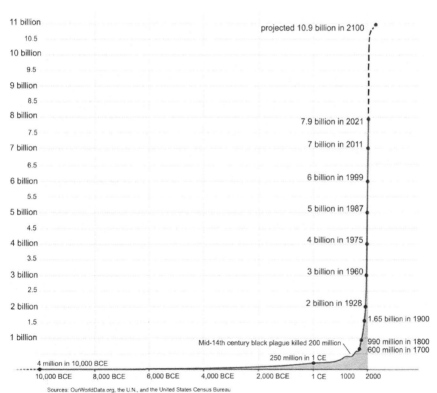

Sources: OurWorldData.org, the U.N., and the United States Census Bureau

4

The Sixth Extinction

When Charles Darwin arrived on the Falkland Islands in the South Atlantic near the tip of South America in 1834, he was puzzled by what he found. The only terrestrial mammal on the islands was a strangely tame dog-like creature. In his journal, Darwin wrote, "It struck me as an outstanding mystery in natural history." He couldn't imagine how the creatures' ancestors could have gotten there. The islands are some 400 miles off the coast of mainland South America—way too long a distance for the creatures to swim. No such animal existed on the mainland of South America anyway. Plus, since there were no other land mammals on the islands, there were no rodents. So, how did it survive?

Recent DNA analysis indicates that the creatures' ancestors had split from a close relative on the mainland around 16,300 years ago. That is probably when it made its way to the Falklands, before further evolving independently. At that time, Earth was in an ice age. The sea level would have been considerably lower, and the islands much bigger and closer to the mainland. So, an ice bridge of just a few miles could have provided the means for a pair or a group of foxlike mammals to make the trip, while being too daunting of a trek for rodents. The Falkland Islands "wolf" had evidently been thriving on crabs, seal pups, shorebirds, and penguins ever since.[1]

Looking somewhat like a cross between a fox and a wolf, the creature was first called "loup-renard" (French for "wolf-fox") by Louis Antoine de Bougainville, a French explorer who established the first settlement on East Falkland in 1764. The creature would come to be most commonly called the "Falkland Islands wolf." But it was also sometimes called the "Falkland Islands fox" or "Falkland Islands dog."

As a result of DNA analysis, we now know the species belongs to a distant branch on the evolutionary tree of dogs. The scientific name assigned was *Dusicyon australis*, meaning "the foolish dog of the south." "Foolish," because it failed to recognize the danger posed by humans.[2]

When explorers and settlers came to the islands, the dogs would sometimes swim out to meet the approaching boats with their tales wagging. They had never experienced any predators, so they had no fear of humans. They could easily be lured to a person holding meat, and then be bludgeoned or stabbed to death.[3]

Falkland Island dogs were killed for their unique fur and poisoned by settlers who feared they would be a threat to their sheep. As Darwin noted in his journal in 1834, "Within a very few years after these islands shall have become regularly settled, in all probability this fox will be classed with the dodo, as an animal which has perished from the face of the earth." Darwin was correct, of course. The last of the Falkland Islands dogs would be killed within 40 years.

The largest marsupial carnivore that Australia's European settlers ever witnessed was the thylacine, at a mere 20 to 30 inches long, plus about a 25-inch tail, and weighing from 35 to 65 pounds. The species name was *Thylacinus cynocephalus*, which roughly translates as "dog-headed pouched one." The thylacine is more commonly known as the Tasmanian tiger, not because it was a cat, but because of the tiger-like stripes on its back. Thylacines were, in fact, much more like a dog.

Thylacines shared a common ancestor with eutherian (placental) canids about 160 million years ago, before the split of placental and marsupial mammals.[4] Their resemblance to modern dogs (except for the stripes and the pouch) is a clear case of convergent evolution. (Convergent evolution is when animals evolve into very similar forms because they evolve in very similar ecological niches, completely independent of one another.)

Fossil evidence indicates thylacines once roamed across Australia before becoming extinct on the mainland about 3,000 years ago, probably as a result of the more capable placental dingoes Asian seafarers had brought to the continent. However, a population that had become isolated as a result of sea level rise about 14,000 years ago continued to thrive on the island of Tasmania, until European settlers arrived.

Thylacines were semi-nocturnal and quite shy, usually avoiding human contact. But habitat destruction and the intro-duction of diseases, such as mange, began to reduce their numbers. The settlers perceived thylacines as a threat to their livestock and treated them as pests. As a result, the local government sponsored their eradication, offering a £1.00 bounty for each thylacine killed.

The species was assigned protective status in 1936, but it was too late. The last remaining thylacine, named "Benjamin," died from neglect in the Hobart Zoo on the 7th of September, 1936.[5]

Perhaps the first instance in which humans altered the planet in a permanent way was our facilitation of the extinction of Australia's and New Guinea's largest animals. When *Homo sapiens* discovered New Guinea and the Australian continent, about 65,000 years ago, they were inhabited by six-foot, 450-pound kangaroos, giant koalas, marsupial lions, mihirungs (flight-less birds about twice the size of

ostriches), and diprotodons (two-and-a-half-ton wombat-like creatures—the largest marsupials the world has ever known).

Soon after the arrival of humans, these giants, along with
some very large lizards and snakes, began to disappear. Within a few
thousand years, they were all gone. Paleontologists have found that
wherever early humans migrated across the planet, extinctions soon
followed—particularly extinctions of the largest animals, known as
"megafauna." As historian Yuval Noah Harari wrote, "*Homo sapiens*
drove to extinction about half of the planet's big beasts long before
humans invented the wheel, writing, or iron tools."[6]

Within 2,000 years after the arrival of humans in the Americas, mammoths, mastodons, native horses, camels, over-sized lions,
saber-tooth cats, giant armadillos and rodents, and ground sloths
weighing up to eight tons and standing as much as twenty feet tall
were all lost. "North America lost thirty-four out of its forty-seven
genera of large mammals. South America lost fifty out of Sixty."[7]

The North and Central American mastodon disappeared
around 11 thousand years ago. Not long to follow was the woolly
mammoth, once common in Siberia and North America. While environmental factors may have been partly to blame for the loss of
these and other large animals, it is likely they were ultimately driven
to extinction by human harvesting for their meat, fur, bones, and
tusks. In North America, a spear tip made of bone has been found
embedded in the rib of a mastodon that died 13,800 years ago.[8] In
Siberia, dwellings constructed of woolly mammoth bones have been
uncovered that date as far back as 25,000 years ago, well before the
end of the last major ice age.[9]

Much like Falkland Island dogs, the megafauna of Australia,
New Guinea, and North and South America had no fear of humans
when they arrived because the animals had not evolved in the
presence of humans. Thus, they could be easily harvested. The large
animals of Africa, on the other hand, evolved alongside humans and

knew to be wary of them. By the time guns and other tools were invented to more easily harvest large game, African tribal traditions of conservation had developed to honor and preserve many of the largest beasts. Today, those traditions are being tested by cultural forces from inside and outside of the continent.

While regrettable, the extinction of mastodons, woolly mammoths, and other large animals (as well as perhaps Falkland Island dogs and thylacines) is not really all that out of the ordinary. A multitude of species have come and gone for billions of years as a result of any number of factors, including the competition or the predation of other species.

Naturally, as human populations have grown, we have used Earth's natural resources, including its living creatures, for our sustenance and for comfort. Unlike other species, however, humans have the capacity to reason. We have an exceptional ability to plan ahead and to conserve for the future. We also have the capacity to comprehend the plight of other creatures that experience fear, pain, suffering, and misery, and to be sympathetic—to be compassionate and merciful in our harvesting of them, if we choose. Too often, we have chosen otherwise.

In the introduction, we saw how explorers and traders had hunted the great auk to extinction because the birds were so easy to catch and because little thought was given to conservation. Though not completely driven to extinction, the Southern Hemisphere's penguins were also subjected to the strains of human consumption and brutality in the 18th and 19th centuries. In his delightful 2007 book, *Penguins of the World*, Wayne Lynch described the 18 species of penguins living today in prose and beautiful pictures. In an appendix, however, Lynch provided an account of the penguins' historic interaction with human beings—another example of the brutality and carelessness with which people have exploited the world's natural resources.

It began with a chance discovery by Captain James Cook in 1775. The famous explorer was the first to report the multitudes of Antarctic fur seals that crammed the beaches of South Georgia. For the next century, wooden ships reeking of blood and death rolled and pitched across every corner of the Southern Ocean. Millions of fur seals were skinned for their luxuriant pelts and countless elephant seals were butchered and boiled for their precious lard.

At first, on the treeless islands where the sealers slaughtered their quarry, penguins were killed as cordwood to fuel the boiling pots. But when the numbers of blubbery seals began to dwindle, the abundant birds became the logical substitute. In just two years, 1864 to 1866, 63,000 gallons (238,500 l) of penguin oil were shipped from the port of Stanley, in the Falkland Islands. Since it takes the boiled bodies of at least eight rockhoppers to yield a gallon of oil (two per liter), that means roughly 500,000 penguins were killed and cooked. In the next 14 years, as many as 1.5 million rockhoppers were tossed into digesters and rendered into lamp oil.

The glint of gold has often spurred humankind to heights of barbarity. Soon after the first sealers arrived on Macquarie Island in the 1820s, hundreds of thousands of royal and king penguins were sentenced to a hideous death. The men herded droves of the terrified and defenseless birds up makeshift wooden ramps. Many of the penguins were year-old birds, called "fats," that had returned to the security of the island to molt. At the end of the gangplank, the hapless birds tumbled into caldrons of boiling oil. Imagine the noise, the stench and the spectacle. But it wasn't sudden enlightenment that halted the slaughter; it was just the decline of profit as penguin numbers slumped below commercially viable levels.[10]

Thankfully, rockhopper, king, and royal penguin populations have largely recovered, and modern public sentiment would prevent commercial enterprises from engaging in that kind of cruelty and overharvesting of the world's beloved penguins. (The absence of a market for lamp oil likely plays a role in sparing them as well.) As we have seen with whales in recent years, if there is enough profit in it, humans continue to be willing to harvest magnificent creatures to extinction. The biggest threats to penguins these days, however, are the loss of their breeding grounds and food sources as a result of climate change. (More about that later.)

The cruelty of human beings is certainly not limited to other creatures. Human history is replete with acts of barbarism between clans of people pitted against each other. Indeed, that was one of the primary reasons for the near extinction of the American bison.

When Columbus arrived on the shores of North America, as many as 30 million bison roamed the great plains of the continent, from the Appalachian Mountains to the Rocky Mountains, from Texas to central Canada. By some accounts, bison occupied as much as two-thirds of the continent.

For numerous Native American tribes, bison were a primary source of meat and of skins for apparel, tent making, and other uses. After the introduction of firearms and horses, some tribes began killing larger numbers for the export of "buffalo robes" and meat. A drought from 1845 to the 1860s also added pressure to some bison populations.

Then, commercial bison hunting began in earnest, often with logistical support from the U.S. Army. The animals were hunted for their fur, meat, and bones. Many were killed simply for sport and left to rot where they fell.

The U.S. Army endorsed the wholesale slaughter of bison in order to deprive Native Americans of their primary food source. General William T. Sherman sought to employ much the same tactic to defeat Native Americans that he had used in the Civil War with his "scorched earth" march to the sea. In 1869, the Army-Navy Journal reported: "General Sherman remarked, in conversation the other day, that the quickest way to compel the Indians to settle down to civilized life was to send ten regiments of soldiers to the plains, with orders to shoot buffaloes until they became too scarce to support the redskins."[11]

There is no evidence that Sherman's idea was implemented, but military commanders were given free-rein to kill as many bison as they could in order to "do their part" in gaining control of Native American tribes. General Sherman and General Philip Sheridan provided opportunities for wealthy hunters to travel west and hunt bison, using U.S. Calvary guns alongside generals like William F. Cody (Buffalo Bill), who earned his nickname after claiming to have personally killed 4,000 bison.*

Ironically, by 1883, it was General Sheridan and Buffalo Bill Cody who began an effort to save the bison from extinction, as most of the last of them were being hunted in Yellowstone National Park. In a letter published in the New York Sun, Cody urged Congress to protect bison in the park, writing, "Their slaughter has been criminally large and useless."[12]

By 1889, only about 1,000 bison remained alive—256 in captivity, 200 protected in Yellowstone, and the rest in the wild, mostly in the Canadian Northwest Territories.[13] Under government and private protection since then, their numbers have increased and

---

* Though commonly called "buffalo," the American bison is not a buffalo. Actual buffalo are only found in Africa and Southeast Asia. Similarly, Native Americans are not Indians. Those are found in India. The term is simply the legacy of Christopher Columbus' miscalculation. He thought he had found another route to India.

they are now classified as "Near Threatened." In 2016, President Obama made bison the first "official mammal of the United States," by signing the National Bison Legacy Act into law.

While many of the world's most vulnerable species are protected by law today, poachers continue to threaten great creatures, like rhinoceroses; both Asian and African elephants; both mountain and lowland gorillas; snow leopards; tigers; panda and polar bears; sea turtles (leatherback, hawksbill, and Kemp's Ridley); North Atlantic and North Pacific right whales; blue whales; vaquita porpoises; and many others. Human depravity induces some of us to harvest endangered species as trophies to stoke needy egos, but most of today's species extinction stems not from blatant callousness and greed, not from unscrupulous operators, but from the sheer magnitude of our numbers and what we all take from nature.

In her 2008 doctoral thesis, marine ecologist and now Associate Professor of History and Environmental Studies at the University of Victoria, Loren McClenachan documented a reduction in the sizes of sport fish caught off the shore of South Florida over a period of 50 years, from 1956 to 2007. Professor McClenachan compared photographs of the prize catches over those years, mostly as seen on the same dock and from the same two charter companies. Since the display boards had not changed over the decades she studied, she was able to accurately measure the sizes of the fish that had been caught and displayed in the photos. The change in fish sizes over those 50 years was remarkable.[14]

After examining 1,275 various trophy fish, McClenachan found that the biggest fish in the 1950s were typically from six to six and a half feet long. Fish sizes were then seen to decline over the years. By 2007, the biggest fish were little more than one foot long. The typical body weight of the fish had dropped by a staggering 88 percent. In her summary, McClenachan noted, "This case study reflects local changes in reef fish communities around Key West,

Florida, but anecdotal evidence suggests that similar declines in populations of large fish have occurred throughout the southeast region and along both coasts of the United States."[15]

McClenachan explained that sport fishing alone could not account for the changes of the reef fishes studied. While recreational fishing contributed, commercial fishing certainly had a larger impact. Furthermore, "commercial fishing for reef sharks in the 1930s and 1940s reduced shark populations before the 1950s, and large groupers have been commercially fished since at least the 1880s."[16]

As demand for seafood has grown in concert with human population growth, natural fish populations around the world have become increasingly depleted, and threats to endangered collateral species have grown. Noting our ancient history as hunter-gatherers, science journalist Gaia Vince aptly observed, "Fish are the last wild animal that we hunt in large numbers. And yet, we may be the last generation to do so."[17]

As marine biologist, oceanographer, and National Geographic Explorer Sylvia Earle explained in her introduction to the 2018 republication of Rachel Carson's classic book, *The Sea Around Us*,

> From the middle of the twentieth century to the present time, the world's human population has more than doubled, while populations of sharks, tunas, swordfish, and many other sea creatures have plummeted by 90 percent. Cities, farms, factories, and fishing fleets have proliferated, while coral reefs, mangrove forests, and sea grass meadows have diminished by half.[18]

According to the UN Food and Agriculture Organization, "a third of commercial fish stocks are being harvested at biologically unsustainable levels and 90 percent are fully exploited." As an example, "the population of Pacific bluefin tuna has plunged 97 percent from historic levels due to rampant overfishing of one of the ocean's most ecologically and economically valuable top predators."[19]

As shark numbers worldwide have plummeted, at least one-third of shark species are at risk of extinction. Such a dramatic reduction of these important predators is creating imbalances in smaller fishes and other marine life, all the way down to plankton. Without plankton and other tiny creatures in the sea, the entire ecosystem begins to fail.[20]

Researchers at the University of British Columbia estimated that, in 2018, China provided about 7.2 billion dollars in subsidies to its fleet of some 3,000 fishing trawlers. Another study found that nearly half of the world's fish harvested in 2014 was taken by Chinese and Taiwanese ships.[21] Of course, those two nations are home to nearly 1.5 billion people (about 19 percent of the world's population) who like to eat fish.

To keep up with demand, fishing trawlers around the world are using increasingly productive practices, including ever-larger-scale bottom trawling—a practice that is destructive to the sea bed and to many more creatures than just the intended harvest, collateral creatures referred to as "by-catch." The vessels can scoop up hundreds of thousands of pounds of fish in each day of operation and, in the process, kill tens of thousands of by-catch while degrading the habitats that produce the fish.

Efforts have been made to erect international treaties to limit subsidies to harmful fishing practices, and to instead direct resources toward the sustainable management of fisheries. As researcher Rashid Sumaila explained, "The politics of this is very hard, but it's important for scientists to continue to show how [harmful subsidies are] not working for society."[22]

Pollution and acidification are also affecting the world's marine ecosystems. Ocean acidification is mainly caused by carbon dioxide in the atmosphere being absorbed into the water and thereby forming carbonic acid. So, as atmospheric CO_2 levels rise, so does the acidity of the oceans. Since the Industrial Revolution began, a little over 200 years ago, the acidity of our oceans has increased by about 30 percent,[23] and rising atmospheric CO_2 levels are continually adding to the problem.

Rising ocean acidity is making it more difficult for those creatures that make shells of calcium carbonate to accomplish that life-dependent task. It affects other sea life too, disrupting some species ability to detect predators or to find suitable habitats.

Of course, rising atmospheric CO_2 is also causing a warming of the entire planet, including the oceans. As the seas warm, local ecosystems are changed. Some creatures move to cooler water or adapt to different habitats, while others simply die.

Coastal waters are also affected by a variety of pollutants that wash into the sea from land, ranging from pesticides and fertilizers, to raw agricultural and human sewage. Ocean dumping from ships and offshore oil and gas operations also contribute to the degradation of marine ecosystems.

Untreated human and agricultural sewage contain harmful pathogens. These can seep into ground water or, more commonly, run off into rivers and streams that make their way to the sea. When bottom feeders consume sewage, they become toxic to other sea creatures and to the humans who eat them. Because of these pathogens and bacteria that flourish in warmer waters, raw oysters—a popular treat on the Texas Gulf Coast just a couple of decades ago—are now much less commonly risked.

The runoff of fertilizers, both from lawns and from commercial agriculture, causes "nutrient pollution." These excessive nutrients regularly cause algae blooms that deplete oxygen from the water and result in "dead zones" along coastal ecosystems around much of the world.[24]

Of course, it is not just sea life that is disappearing at alarming rates. The *Living Planet Index* (LPI) is a collection of scientific studies that are included in the *Living Planet Report* (LPR), published bi-annually by the Zoological Society of London and the World Wildlife Fund. The LPI tracks almost 21,000 populations of mammals, birds, amphibians, reptiles, and fish around the world. While varied among species and locales, the 2020 report revealed that, between 1970 and 2016, the wildlife populations studied had declined by an average of 68 percent.[25]

The tropical subregions of Latin America and the Caribbean saw the most dramatic wildlife population decline at 94 percent, with freshwater fish, reptiles, and amphibians most affected. The primary causes are habitat loss and human-transported diseases.

Since the arrival of Portuguese colonists in 1500, the Atlantic Forest in Brazil has lost 87 percent of its natural vegetation to timber harvesting and clearing for agricultural tracts and human settlement, with most of that loss occurring within the last 100 years. As a result, the populations of all species that resided in the forest have been decimated.

South American amphibians are also being ravaged by chytrid fungus, believed to have been inadvertently brought from Africa by traders in the 1930s. The fungus continues to spread through ever-decreasing amphibian populations. Within the Atlantic Forest, at least two species have been lost and another 46 species are threatened. In the highlands of central Panama, the chytrid fungus has led to the loss of 30 amphibian species. All told, more than 2,000 remaining amphibian species are threatened with extinction.[26]

The more widely a species population is dispersed, the more it is protected from the spread of disease, as well as other calamities.

As habitats are destroyed and wildlife are prevented from moving as a result of clear-cuts, highways, and cities, smaller and less widely dispersed species populations are becoming more vulnerable to extinction. As wildlife populations have plummeted, quite a few species have already been lost. Furthermore, the number of documented terrestrial plant extinctions has been twice that of mammals, birds, and amphibians combined.[27]

There are at least five threats to biodiversity and the preservation of species: land use change (primarily deforestation), climate change, overharvesting, pollution, and the introduction of invasive species (both intentionally and inadvertently) and diseases. According to the *Living Planet Report*, in the coming decades, these pressures will threaten the extinction of an estimated one million animal species—500,000 insect and 500,000 other species.[28]

Insects may seem to be an annoyance much of the time, but they are crucial to our world and to our way of life. They condition soils and recycle nutrients. They break down animal and plant waste. In many ways, insects serve as the base of the food chain, as they are eaten by reptiles, small mammals, birds, and fish. They pollinate about three-fourths of all flowering plants, including food crops. American biologist E.O. Wilson described them as "the little things that run the world."

To date, more than one million insect species have been identified. Estimates are that another 4.5 million of them, mostly in the tropics, have yet to be formally described. Insects include a wider range of species than any other class of animal. Many of them are disappearing around the world. For example, insect populations that were studied in German grassland and forest sites between 2008 and 2017 shrank by a staggering 78 percent in just those nine years.[29]

There is one group of insects that is most crucial to our food supply and in great peril—bees. Both wild and domestic bees are becoming increasingly threatened.

In 2007, worker honey bees began to just disappear, leaving behind the queen, unhatched larvae, and plenty of honey for a few remaining nurse bees to care for the queen and the larvae. Industrial and small-scale bee keepers alike suffered significant losses. There had been anecdotal tales of bee disappearances before, but the 2007 event marked first use of the term "colony collapse disorder" or CCD. The incidents and severity of CCD have declined in recent years, but remain a significant concern. That decline can likely be attributed to better pesticide management.

The precise causes of colony collapse disorder are not fully understood, but the probable causes are parasites, a virus, and a diminished resistance to those hazards resulting from pesticides like neonicotinoids (extremely toxic to all bees), herbicides, habitat loss or fragmentation, and uncommon temperature fluctuations. Of course, it is not just honey bees that are in peril. Bumblebees have also been found to suffer from pesticides, herbicides, habitat loss, and climate change.

Bumblebees are among the most important pollinators. They fertilize a wide range of wild plants, many of our favorite flowers, and important food crops, including potatoes, blueberries, strawberries, squash, cucumbers, peppers, melons, tomatoes, and many others. By one estimate, pollinated food crops account for about one trillion dollars in global agricultural product sales each year.

A recent study conducted by the University of Ottawa has tracked bumblebee population decline in a wide range of locations in Europe and North America. Researchers examined 66 bumblebee species populations across the two continents. Published in the journal *Science*, the study's summary explained that climate change is likely to be a significant driver of bumblebee population declines. It found that in areas that had become hotter or areas that experienced dramatic temperature fluctuations, bumblebees were less abundant than in previous years, before the temperature anomalies.[30]

Scientists have noted that climate change is only one among many factors that account for why insect populations are plummeting. Exeter University ecologist Matthias Becher explained, "While bees might be able to cope with one stressor alone, the combination of several stressors may bring a population over the tipping point."[31] Whatever the causes, the loss of insects, along with the losses of sea life and terrestrial wildlife, are undoubtedly a threat to our own way of life. These losses threaten the resources upon which we depend, as well as our ability to live in a world filled with amazing creatures.

Well known, of course, is the plight of polar bears. Today there are from 20,000 to 30,000 polar bears in 19 different groups across Alaska, Northern Canada, Greenland, Norway, and Siberia. Several of those groups are known to be in decline, while others appear to be stable or have not yet been assessed. Most studied are bears in the Beaufort Sea region, above Alaska and Canada, where populations have declined by 40 percent in just the last ten years. The primary cause is believed to be the loss of sea ice.[32]

Polar bears rely almost exclusively on a high-calorie diet of seals, and their ability to catch those seals is dependent on sea ice. The bears conserve energy by "still-hunting." That is, waiting for hours beside the breathing holes of seals. When a seal comes up for air, the bear will slap it with both front paws to stun it. She will then bite the seal by the neck and pull it onto the ice to feed herself and her cubs. "They're far more successful doing this than any other method of hunting," explained Anthony Pagano, a wildlife biologist with the U.S. Geological Survey, whose teams have studied the bears.[33]

Polar bears are high-metabolism carnivores, normally burning well over 12,000 calories per day. When the sea ice is broken up, the bears have to run and/or swim in their efforts to catch a seal, burning many more calories. After repeated failures, the animals are weakened and even less able to catch a seal.

As seasonal sea ice has melted earlier each year, bears have been forced to swim great distances to reach seal colonies. Blaine Griffen, a biologist and associate professor at Brigham Young University, described the struggle of a female that had been tracked by researchers. She swam 426 miles over nine days in search of seals. The trek resulted in a loss of 22 percent of her body weight and, most tragically, the loss of her cub that had begun the journey with her.[34]

Earth's poles are warming even faster than the rest of the planet, and the Arctic has been losing sea ice at a rate of about 13.1 percent per decade since 1981.[35] Naturally, as Arctic Sea ice continues to disappear, so will polar bears.

At the other end of the planet, the loss of sea ice along the western Antarctic Peninsula is similarly affecting several penguin species. Emperor penguins, for example, raise their chicks on the ice of the seasonally frozen Antarctic Ocean, amid harsh winter conditions. Emperors are the largest, heaviest, and best-known of the penguin species. They are the only species that dare to breed during the winter, when Antarctic temperatures can dip as low as minus 73 degrees Fahrenheit and winds can blow up to 120 miles per hour. The birds huddle in groups of up to several hundred individuals to shield the juveniles from the elements.

Emperor penguin couples mate monogamously for the season and often for life. The male has the sole duty of incubating a single egg each season by balancing it on his feet to keep it off the ice and by covering it with his body—fasting throughout the entire two-month incubation period. The female will return to the breeding site when the egg is hatched with a belly full of food to regurgitate for the hatchling, while the male returns to the sea to get food for himself. If the seasonal sea ice breaks up too early, before the young chick has sufficiently matured and grown its waterproof feathers, it can easily be swept into the sea to die. As a result of shorter periods of seasonal ice on the peninsula, several Emperor penguin colonies have already suffered significant population declines.[36] Further warming of the poles will undoubtedly put these magnificent creatures, among others, at risk of extinction.

Adélie penguins breed and raise their chicks on areas of dry shoreline on the Antarctic Peninsula, building nests from pebbles. Warmer temperatures have resulted in more moisture in the air and, thus, more snowfall, making it harder for the birds to find suitable nesting sites. Though they do not nest on the ice, Adélie penguins are nevertheless dependent on it. They will eat fish and squid, but their primary diet is krill. Krill feed on algae on the bottom of sea ice. So, less ice means less krill. Exacerbating their problems, warmer weather is enabling the southward migration of ice-intolerant Chinstrap and Gentoo penguins into the Adélie breeding areas.[37] As a result of these pressures, some populations of Adélie penguins have declined by more than 90 percent.

Even penguins that live in temperate climates are suffering from global warming. Galápagos penguins and other species on the coasts of South America and South Africa, live there because of abundant food supplies that are brought to the ocean surface by cold water currents. During El Niño events, however, warmer water prevents those cold currents from reaching the surface, and climate change is increasing the occurrence of those events.

"Following the powerful El Niño events of 1982-1983 and 1997-1998, the Galápagos penguin population plummeted by 77 percent and 65 percent respectively, leaving less than 2,000 penguins today."[38] Galápagos penguins are the world's smallest penguin population and are one of the 10 (out of 18) penguin species threatened with extinction.

While quite a few plant and animal species are being decimated by the effects of climate change, a great many others are more successfully adapting. Some types of plants and both terrestrial and aquatic animals are simply moving to higher latitudes or higher altitudes to find cooler temperatures.[39] But, we should not underestimate the costs of the world's changing climate. Aside from the loss of many of the world's most beautiful and magnificent creatures, many of the costs will be direct financial losses and health risks to ourselves, as we will see in the following chapter.

At the conclusion of her Pulitzer Prize-winning book, *The Sixth Extinction*, Elizabeth Kolbert noted an exhibit in the American Museum of Natural History's Hall of Biodiversity. Using the fossils of extinct species, the exhibit illustrates Earth's five large-scale extinction events that have occurred since the emergence of complex organisms. At the center of the exhibit is a plaque with a cursory explanation for the devastation: "Global climate change and other causes, probably including collisions between Earth and extraterrestrial objects." The plaque goes on to declare, "Right now we are in the midst of the Sixth Extinction, this time caused solely by humanity's transformation of the ecological landscape."

Kolbert described the implication of the exhibit—that we (humankind) have put ourselves at risk of extinction by a lack of care and foresight in our use of Earth's natural resources.

The logic behind this way of thinking runs as follows: having freed ourselves from the constraints of evolution, humans nevertheless remain dependent on the earth's biological and geochemical systems. By disrupting these systems—cutting down tropical rainforests, altering the composition of the atmosphere, acidifying the oceans— we're putting our own survival in danger.[40]

She then noted a sign that hangs in the Hall of Biodiversity at Stanford University that quotes ecologist Paul Ehrlich proclaiming: "In pushing other species to extinction, humanity is busy sawing off the limb on which it is perched."[41]

Despite such pessimistic sentiments, there may be hope. Given the remarkable inventiveness and ingenuity of human beings, it seems quite unlikely that we, as a species, will go extinct as a result of our own making anytime soon.

As we will see in Chapter 8, quite a lot is already being done to mitigate the risks to wildlife, to regulate commercial fishing, to manage forests, to regulate the use of pesticides and fertilizers, to recycle plastics, to reduce greenhouse gas emissions, and to "green" our cities. While the things being done are very far from enough, they do suggest at least the possibility of solutions to be imagined and implemented.

But, of course, this all hinges on what we choose to do. It hinges on the kind of world in which we choose to live. It hinges on which political leaders we elect to lead the way.

It is not necessarily our survival that is at stake, it is our way of life. If we wish to live in a world filled with beauty, wonder, and inspiration—a world filled with magnificent creatures—we can look only to ourselves to take responsibility for just such a world.

5

A Torrid Future

I n the summer of 2019, reports began to emerge that President
Donald Trump had been looking into the plausibility of the
United States buying Greenland. Many people were surprised by the
idea and attributed it to Trump's naivety and his history of real
estate speculating. Despite becoming a punchline of jokes at
Trump's expense, the United States buying Greenland is really not
such a crazy idea. We need only look to the outcome of the purchase
of Alaska in the mid-nineteenth century.

In March of 1867, the United States reached an agreement to
purchase the territory of Alaska from Russia. The treaty for the
purchase was negotiated and signed by Secretary of State William
Seward and Russian Minister to the United States Edouard de
Stoeckl. The transaction soon became known as "Seward's Folly" or
"Seward's Icebox" deal, as a great many people failed to recognize
the value of the territory. The ridicule began to subside, however,
when gold was discovered in the Yukon in 1896 and Alaska became
the gateway to the Klondike gold fields. In addition to forestalling a
Russian foothold on the North American continent, the purchase
ultimately provided an abundance of natural resources for the
United States at a cost of only 7.2 million dollars.[1]

Greenland would also be a valuable asset to the United States
in terms of both natural resources and strategic advantage[2]—more

so now than at any time in history. Its resources include iron ore, lead, zinc, copper, gold, diamonds, rubies, sapphire, rare-earth elements, uranium, and oil. As Greenland's Ministry of Foreign Affairs tweeted, "Greenland is rich in natural resources such as minerals, the purest water and ice, fish stocks, seafood, renewable energy, and is a new frontier for adventure tourism." The ministry then added, "We're open for business, not for sale."

Trump was not the first president to contemplate buying Greenland. President Andrew Jackson's administration had raised the idea in the 1830s. An 1867 U.S. State Department report suggested it too. In 1946, President Harry Truman offered Denmark $100 million for the island, but no deal was struck.[3]

Aside from its extremely cold temperatures, Greenland's rough terrain is mostly covered in snow and thick glaciers—over two miles thick in some places—making extraction of its resources difficult. But that is changing. A warming planet is melting Greenland and unlocking its treasures.

Perhaps most significantly in the short term, the melting of the polar ice cap is opening up new North Atlantic shipping lanes along Greenland's west coast for commerce and for warships. Instead of having to pass through the Suez or Panama Canals, ships are able to travel from ocean to ocean by way of Canada's* Northwest Passage more safely and for more months each summer.

There will likely be a few other benefits to the warming of our planet. There could be a decrease in mortality from severe cold waves. Some mid-latitude regions will increase crop yields with warmer weather and increased precipitation. High-latitude regions may be able to grow crops that previously were not possible. Portions of Canada's prairies could become a wheat-growing belt. Citrus fruits could be grown in the Midwest, the United Kingdom, and Northern Europe. Studies have shown that, up to a certain point,

---

* Canada claims sovereignty of the passage, but the United States and other nations proclaim the passage to be international waters.

some food crops grow better and can be more drought tolerant with higher levels of CO_2 in the air.[4] (Of course, what's good for some food crops is also good for weeds.)

Manmade global warming might even help to mitigate the negative effects of a "Mini Ice Age," an event that some people say is forthcoming. The sun regularly goes through 11-year cycles of higher and lower energy output. Occasionally, the sun's activity settles down for an extended period called a "Grand Solar Minimum." The last time this occurred, from about 1650 to 1715, it corresponded with a "Little Ice Age" in Earth's Northern Hemisphere. It is widely believed that extremely low solar activity in combination with an increase of volcanic aerosols resulted in the lower surface temperatures. Some people believe we are due for another extended Grand Solar Minimum, and that it will result in another Mini Ice Age. The National Aeronautics and Space Administration (NASA), on the other hand, says "no."

NASA has calculated the correlation between Total Solar Irradiance (the sun's light energy output reaching Earth's surface) and global average temperatures back to 1880. While some apparent correlation can be seen until around 1950, rising global temperatures since that time have not corresponded with solar irradiance. Instead, they have been driven by factors here on Earth that have far outweighed the effects of varying solar activity. According to NASA,

> The warming caused by the greenhouse gas emissions from human burning of fossil fuels is **six times greater** than the possible decades-long cooling from a prolonged Grand Solar Minimum. Even if a Grand Solar Minimum were to last a century, global temperatures would continue to warm.[5]

Furthermore, the latest observations by NASA and NOAA have revealed that the sun is currently ramping up its activity and is expected to peak in 2025, with dramatic displays of solar flares, sunspots, and outbursts of charged solar material called "coronal mass ejections." (We should be on the lookout for increasingly beautiful Northern Lights for the next few years, and for a total eclipse in 2024 when the displays will be the most observable.)[6]

All indications are that we are on a course of warming that will increasingly change the character of our planet and present significant challenges for our future.

Unfortunately, the hazards of a warming planet far outweigh the benefits. As Greenland melts and the Northwest Passage becomes more easily navigable, the seas are rising. Researchers at NASA's Jet Propulsion Laboratory in Southern California explained, "Greenland's melting glaciers, which plunge into Arctic waters via steep-sided inlets, or fjords, are among the main contributors to global sea level rise."[7]

Glaciers extending from Greenland's vast ice sheet travel slowly down valleys into fjords, where they melt and "calve" (break off) as icebergs. Snowfall replenishes the ice sheet as it is compacted over time. Since the 1990s, however, the melting and calving have significantly outpaced the replenishment from snowfall.

Glacier melt is driven by two factors—rising air temperatures and rising seawater temperatures in a process called "undercutting." Rising air temperatures in summer result in meltwater that flows through crevasses or boreholes created by the warming into rivers below the surface of the ice and eventually reaches the sea. The meltwater is less dense than salty seawater, so it rises in plumes, mixing with warm seawater and licking the base of the glaciers.

NASA researcher Michael Wood described the findings of recent studies: "The biggest and deepest glaciers are undercut much faster than the smaller glaciers in shallow water. In other words, the biggest glaciers are the most sensitive to warming waters, and those are the ones really driving Greenland's ice loss."[8] Ice loss varies from year to year, but 2019 set a record with 586 billion tons of ice breaking off and melting into the sea—enough to cover the entire state of California in four feet of water.[9]

Albeit at a slower pace so far, the same thing is happening in Antarctica, which holds 90 percent of our planet's ice—enough to raise sea levels by 200 feet.[10] Global sea levels will not likely rise anywhere near that amount any time soon, but an accelerating loss of ice in Antarctica warrants our attention.

Antarctica is divided by the Transantarctic Mountains into two unequal portions. Making up less than a third of the continent, West Antarctica holds enough ice to raise global sea levels by about 17 feet. That is where the most dramatic changes have been observed in recent decades, changes that are occurring at an accelerating pace. "A recent review by nearly 100 polar scientists—known as the Ice Sheet Mass Balance Intercomparison Exercise, or IMBIE—shows that from 2012 to 2017, West Antarctica lost some 159 billion tons of ice annually, more than twice the rate of the early 2000s."[11]

The topography of West Antarctica has facilitated much of its melting. Large portions of the West's bedrock are below sea level under massive ice shelves. As seawater temperatures and levels have risen, the shelves are melting from below and breaking away. Massive glaciers behind them then flow downward toward the sea, feeding ice into the melting process.

East Antarctica, on the other hand, is well above sea level. It is home to the South Pole and the coldest temperatures and the thickest ice on Earth, reaching temperatures as low as minus 144 degrees Fahrenheit (-98 degrees Celsius) and with ice over three miles thick. Containing ten times more ice than the West, East Antarctica's massive ice sheet was formed over tens of millions of years and was long thought to be stable, even growing. Recent studies, however, have revealed net losses of ice there too.

NASA satellite images are showing that East Antarctic glaciers are moving with increasing speed toward the Southern Ocean, where they are dumping ice into the sea at rates higher than new ice is being formed by snowfall in the interior. The biggest among them is the Totten Glacier, which alone could raise sea levels by an estimated 12.6 feet. But this won't likely happen during our lifetime.

The melting of Antarctica will take thousands of years. But even a small portion of that melting will affect the lives of people around the world. Scientists believe that the melting ice of Antarctica could easily add a foot to global mean sea level by the end of this century, and perhaps 3 feet by the middle of the next century. When added to the melting of Greenland's ice and mountain glaciers* around the world, along with the thermal expansion of seawater as it warms, we are likely to see a significant rise in global sea levels by 2100—some scientists say as much as three feet. The U.S. National Oceanic and Atmospheric Administration (NOAA) has warned, "If we follow a pathway with high emissions, a worst-case scenario of as much as 8.2 feet (2.5 meters) above 2000 levels by 2100 cannot be ruled out."[12] A rise of only a couple of feet will be devastating.

Research published in the journal *Nature* indicates that a global sea-level rise** of just under two feet (50-70cm) will directly affect the lives of some 360 million people around the world—200 million whose homes will be under water, and 160 million who will be subjected to significantly more annual flooding from storms. About 70 percent of those are in Asia—mostly China, Bangladesh, India, Vietnam, Indonesia, Thailand, the Philippines, and Japan. More

---

* Montana's Glacier National Park today has 30 glaciers. Most of the more than 150 glaciers that were there in 1910 have melted away.
** The amount of sea level rise can vary from one location to another because of varying winds, ocean currents, temperatures, and seabed depths.

than four million people in the Netherlands will live below sea level, straining the effectiveness of their flood-control systems. Other European countries that will be directly affected are the United Kingdom, Germany, Turkey, France, and Italy.[13] Some island nations, like Kiribati, Tuvalu, the Marshall Islands, the Seychelles, and the Maldives, could be completely lost.[14]

The Maldives consist of 1,190 tiny islands spread over hundreds of square miles of the Indian Ocean and are the home of some 540,000 people. The most densely populated city in the world is Malé, the Maldives' capital, with over 140,000 people living on an island of about 2.5 square miles. Scientists predict that, with sea level rise and the increasing severity of storms, all of the Maldives' islands, as well as the Seychelles, may be uninhabitable by as soon as 2030.[15]

In the United States, nearly 40 percent of the population lives in high-density coastal areas where sea levels play a role in flooding, shoreline erosion, and destructive storm surges.[16] Particularly vulnerable are cities like Miami, Virginia Beach, Atlantic City, New York City, and Boston, not to mention all of the barrier islands and every beach around the country.

Some areas of New Orleans are already below sea level and the city is sinking. A 2016 NASA study found that parts of New Orleans are sinking at a rate of two inches per year. Areas around Houston are also sinking at that same rate.[17] This is making both cities more vulnerable to flooding from tropical storms—storms that are becoming stronger and more numerous as a result of rising seawater temperatures.

In addition to the direct effects on coastal populations, coastal wetlands that nurture crucial ecosystems are also being affected by rising seas, destructive storms, and human activity. The wetlands of Louisiana's Mississippi delta, for example, comprise almost half of the wetlands in the United States and are disappearing at an alarming rate.

Louisiana's wetlands make up one of the world's largest habitats for migratory waterfowl and some 95 percent of all marine species in the Gulf of Mexico spend all or part of their lifecycle there. About 66 percent of the Gulf's sport and commercial fish species are dependent upon wetland ecosystems, and Louisiana's commercial fisheries provide more than 30 percent of the nation's seafood.[18] Wetlands also absorb carbon from the atmosphere at even higher rates than rainforests.[19]

As a result of sea level rise, subsidence, and the construction of levee systems to control flooding, an estimated 25 to 35 square miles of Louisiana's wetlands are being lost each year. The rate of loss has been slowing because of better land management, but more than a million acres of wetlands have already vanished since the early 1900s. "Louisiana's Department of Natural Resources maintains that at current land loss rates, nearly 640,000 more acres, an area the size of Rhode Island, will be under water by 2050."[20]

Research conducted by NOAA suggests it could be even worse, with Louisiana experiencing the highest rate of relative sea-level rise "on the planet" in the coming decades. "When new data on the rate of coastal subsidence is married with updated projections of sea-level rise, the southeast corner of Louisiana looks likely to be under at least 4.3 feet of gulf water by the end of the century."[21]

Just as the glaciers of Greenland and Iceland are melting, so is the permafrost and snow of Greenland, the Northern territories of Canada, Alaska, and Siberia, as well as the seasonal snowfall of winters around the world.

The white snow at the poles and of seasonal snowfalls reflects light and heat back into space, away from Earth—something measured as the albedo* of the planet. As Earth warms, smaller

---

* Astronomers define the reflectivity of objects (such as planets, moons, or asteroids) in space using the term "albedo." This is the amount of electromagnetic radiation that reflects away from the object, compared to the amount that is absorbed. Albedo is measured on a scale from 0 (no reflectivity) to 1 (total reflectivity).

amounts of reflective snow stay on the ground and so more heat is absorbed, creating a feedback loop—more heat melts more snow and brings more heat, which melts more snow and brings more heat, which...

Conversely, a warming planet increases cloud cover which has the opposite effect, as seen by a reversal of albedo from 2001 to 2003. But in the long term, the loss of snow appears to be out-weighing the additional cloud cover. Analyses of Earth's albedo by measuring the Earthshine seen on those portions of the moon not illuminated by the sun have shown a decreasing reflectivity of our planet. As science reporter Fraser Cain of *Universe Today* explained,

> The annual average albedo declined very gradually from 1985 to 1995, then declined sharply in 1995 and 1996. ... The low albedo during 1997-2001 increased solar heating of the globe at a rate more than twice than expected from a doubling of atmospheric carbon dioxide. This "dimming" of Earth, as it would be seen from space, is perhaps connected with the recent accelerated increase in mean global surface temperatures.[22]

Scientists have mused about schemes to increase Earth's albedo in order to reduce global warming—some more practical than others. For example, the roofs of houses and buildings around the world could be whitewashed to make them more reflective. Injecting salt particles into low-level stratocumulus clouds over the oceans could make them brighter and more reflective. Even the idea of launching mirrors into orbit to reflect sunlight before it reaches the atmosphere has been discussed.[23]

A few albedo-increasing human activities around the world have already demonstrated the possibilities, even if unintentionally. The province of Almería on the southern coast of Spain, for example, has the largest concentration of greenhouses in the world, covering as much as 65,000 acres in the driest desert in Europe and providing the continent with an abundance of fruits and vegetables. The "sea of plastic" greenhouses reflects so much light back into the atmosphere that the entire area has experienced a temperature decline of 0.3 degrees Centigrade per decade, while temperatures in the rest of Spain have been rising faster than world averages.[24]

A village in the Peruvian Andes Mountains has been painting the side of a mountain white in a scheme to mitigate the loss of water they had been getting from glacier melt. The glacier that had been their source of water completely melted away in the 1990s. The white areas of mountain side stay cool enough for ice to form on them at night and in colder weather. The hope is that, over time, a small glacier will build up and once again provide them with a source of water for their grazing alpacas.[25]

While schemes to deflect the sun's energy back into space may provide some benefits in the short term, they would certainly fall short of solving all the problems caused by greenhouse gas emissions. Such schemes do nothing to counteract the acidification of our oceans that results from an abundance of carbon dioxide in the atmosphere.

It is difficult to know just how much global warming can be attributed to the declining albedo of Earth, but it appears to be a contributing factor. In any case, declining reflectivity is an observable result of our warming planet—the planet NOAA has found to be warmer in each of the last five years than at any other time in the 139 years NOAA has tracked global temperatures.[26]

Melting permafrost also releases methane and other greenhouse gases into the atmosphere. In 2011, NOAA and the National Snow and Ice Data Center predicted that melting permafrost would soon transform the Arctic from a carbon sink (where carbon is absorbed) to a carbon source. That same study predicted that by 2100, the equivalent of half the carbon ever produced by human activity would be released from the Arctic.[27] This is another feedback loop, where warmer temperatures result in the release of greenhouse gases that, in turn, facilitate further warming.

There are more hazards to human beings from the warming of our planet than just rising sea levels and more powerful and more numerous storms that affect our coastal cities, beaches, and wetlands. Higher temperatures will also dramatically affect the world's diversity of life, our food and fresh water supplies, and the general health of people around the world. The heat alone is killing a lot of people. In fact, extreme heat is already killing more people than tornadoes, hurricanes, and floods combined.[28] And it is getting worse.

A 2015 Columbia University study concluded rising temperatures and humidity attributed to climate change could expose hundreds of millions of people around the world to lethal heat stress by 2060. The greatest dangers will be in the populous tropical regions of Africa, the Middle East, India, and Southeast Asia. Even in the United States, as many as 30 million people in the northeast could be exposed yearly to temperatures that can be lethal to the elderly, people with cardiovascular problems, people who do strenuous labor outside, and children.[29]

Heat waves are killing thousands of people each year. In the summer of 2010, for example, a series of heat waves struck Northern Europe, with the most devastating effect in Russia, where it was reported that "up to 56,000 people died as a result of overheating, droughts, forest fires, and smog."[30] In April and May of 2016, temperatures reached a record 123.8° Fahrenheit in Phalodi, India, killing 160 people and affecting 330 million others. In June of 2015, as many as 2,000 people died in the port city of Karachi, Pakistan when temperatures reached 120° Fahrenheit for several days. A heat wave in June of 2021 killed as many as 200 people in the American Pacific Northwest and 500 people in British Columbia when temperatures exceeded 115° Fahrenheit. It is believed that more than a billion marine animals along the Canadian coast were also killed by the unprecedented temperatures.[31] It may be months or years before all the costs of that event are fully assessed.

In most cases, it is the combination of high temperatures and high humidity that proves lethal. Near bodies of water, rising temperatures push more moisture into the air. So, as both air and water temperatures rise in coastal cities around the world, more people will be vulnerable to heat stroke related deaths—particularly people who do not have air conditioning or who work outside in places like Shanghai, Mumbai, Manila, London, Rio de Janeiro, Miami, Charleston, Atlantic City, New York, New Orleans, and Houston.

In poor agrarian countries the problem is compounded by demanding working conditions. For example, a very high percentage of the sugar cane harvesters in El Salvador suffer from chronic kidney disease, a development of just the last couple of decades. It is believed this is probably the result of prolonged dehydration from working in the increasingly hot and humid fields.[32]

The U.S. Centers for Disease Control and Prevention (CDC) reported that between 2004 and 2018 an average of 702 heat-related deaths occurred each year in the United States.[33] An EPA study released in 2021 concluded that the previous decade saw three times more heat waves than in the 1960s. The study (which had been withheld for several years by the Trump Administration) also noted shrinking Arctic ice, melting permafrost in Alaska, losses of winter ice on the Great Lakes, rising ocean temperatures, and coral bleaching. Pollen and wildfire seasons are "starting earlier and lasting longer." The study explained how rising temperatures had resulted in a 50-year doubling of summer energy use to air condition homes—which, in turn, has increased greenhouse gas emissions that trap more heat in the atmosphere.[34]

As reported in the EPA study, climate change is making wildfires more common, more severe and widespread, and more difficult to extinguish. Wildfires are a natural occurrence, as lightning strikes ignite dry forests and brush. But modern wildfires are more often caused by the carelessness or the depravity of human beings. In either case, climate change is making them more common in some parts of the world and much more destructive than in previous decades.

Fires in Australia from July 2019 through March of 2020 burned more than 46 million acres and killed or destroyed the habitats of nearly three billion animals—51 million amphibians, 143 million mammals, 180 million birds, and 2.46 billion reptiles. The study excluded the incalculable losses of invertebrates like spiders and insects, as well as the aquatic species affected by the runoff of ash into streams and rivers. Lily van Eeden, lead author of the report and researcher at the University of Sydney, said the ten researchers from Australian Universities and wildlife groups who conducted the study could not put an exact figure on how many animals were killed, but the estimate of the losses was "quite conservative."[35]

Seventy-five people died from the flames of bushfires that season, including 13 Victorian CFA* firefighters. Many more, however, died of smoke inhalation and other related ailments. A research team of scholars from the Australian states of Tasmania and New South Wales concluded that 417 people (in the four East Coast states that were studied) died of smoke inhalation, while another 3,000 people were hospitalized for cardiac and respiratory problems. About 1,300 went to emergency rooms for asthma attacks.[36] Many more long-term effects are likely to arise. The fires of that 2019-2020 season also took at least 3,500 homes and thousands of other structures.

In California, the 2020 fire season saw five of the six largest fires in the state's history, destroying 4.1 million acres of dense timber—groves of ancient redwoods, giant sequoias, and more than a million Joshua trees[37]—in addition to some 8,200 homes and other structures, displacing over 53,000 people.[38]

---

* Country Fire Authority is a volunteer fire service in the state of Victoria.

The 2017 California fire season directly killed about 50 people. In 2018, the Camp Fire alone levelled the small town of Paradise and killed 86 people. The massive fires of the 2020 fire season, by comparison, directly took the lives of only 33 people, but a great many more were impacted by the smoke.

Stanford University researcher Marshall Burke explained, "A lot of news coverage focuses on immediate danger: people with homes in harm's way. The impacts are much, much larger than that ... they extend all over the place to people hundreds of miles away from the wildfire." In September of 2020, heavy smoke hung over much of Northern California, including the San Francisco Bay area, where a dark and ominous orange glow filled the skies for several days.[39] Stanford researchers estimated that some 4,800 emergency-room visits and as many as 1,200 early deaths could be attributed to the smoke.[40]

A collaborative study of California's 2018 fire season among several universities, including the University of California, Irvine, revealed an economic cost of about 150 billion dollars—about 0.7 percent of the gross domestic product of the entire United States that year. The research team calculated a direct capital impact (destroyed homes and buildings) of 27.7 billion dollars, health costs of about 32.2 billion dollars, and another 88.6 billion dollars in costs associated with the disruptions of supply chains, transportation, and labor.[41] Of course, that is just one season in California. Wildfires occur all over the world each year and, in many places, changing climates are making them worse. At this writing, it appears that the 2021 fire season may well become much worse than previous years.

Living forests, particularly tropical forests, and all varieties of vegetation absorb carbon dioxide and release oxygen into the atmosphere, reducing the most common greenhouse gas that contributes to global warming. The loss of forests and other vegetation, therefore, facilitates the warming of the planet.

As they decompose, trees and vegetation release the carbon they contain. Forests, woodlands, grasslands, and peat also release carbon when they burn. So, wildfires create another feedback loop, where a warmer planet and associated climate change facilitate more burning, which contributes to a warmer planet, which facilitates more burning, which contributes to...

So-called "zombie fires" in Arctic forests and permafrost are even greater producers of greenhouse gases. The floors of high-latitude forests are often made up of carbon-rich peat, which is composed of dead vegetation, such as shrubs and mosses, and the flotsam of trees and other plants that have not completely decomposed. Peat forms in damp and cold parts of the world, where organic material decomposes very slowly, and can build up over centuries or even many millennia and, in the Arctic, become a part of permafrost.

As Jessica McCarty, an Arctic scientist at Miami University in Ohio, explained, "Arctic fires are burning earlier and farther north, in landscapes previously thought to be fire resistant."[42] "...Much of the peat that is burning, which is as old as 15,000 to 20,000 years, is trapped in permafrost. As ancient permafrost melts, the peat becomes available to burn. And burning it is."

The peat fires to which Professor McCarty was referring can smolder and migrate under the surface for very long periods, even under snow-covered winters, and then flare up again—hence the moniker, "zombie fires." "In 2020, Arctic fires released almost 250 megatons of carbon dioxide, about half as much as Australia emits in a year from human activity and about 2.5 times as much as the record-breaking 2020 California fire season."[43]

Another significant economic impact of continuing climate change will be associated with the transformation of agricultural practices and locales. Warming weather and changing precipitation patterns are moving agricultural productivity from place to place, generally northward, a phenomenon that will become increasingly disruptive and costly. As the United States Department of Agriculture (USDA) has explained,

> The changing climate presents real threats to U.S. agricultural production, forest resources, and rural economies. These threats have significant implications not just for farmers, ranchers, and forest landowners, but for all Americans. Land managers across the country are already feeling the pressures of a changing climate and its effects on weather. As these risks continue and amplify, producers will be faced with the challenges of adapting.[44]

About 90 percent of the 570 million farms around the world are small family-run farms. Many of the farmers are poor and their work is especially vulnerable to changes in seasonal climate. Changes in the timing or the intensity of seasonal rain or the emergence of a prolonged drought can wipe out a family's crops. Climate-associated changes in the behavior or the migration of pollinators also can affect productivity.

Crop pests (as well as mosquitos, ticks, and jellyfish) are thriving in the warmer temperatures. Booming populations of bark beetles have devastated millions of acres of spruce and pine forests. So far, the small rise in yearly average temperatures, in and of itself, has been less of an issue than how that increase in temperatures has affected pollinating and pest insects and, particularly, precipitation patterns.

For example, over the last century in the United States, the Northeast, Midwest, and Great Plains have seen increases in precipitation, while parts of the West, Southwest, and Southeast have seen decreases in precipitation, resulting in a greater severity of occasional droughts.[45]

A recent study found that, since the start of the 21st century, the American Southwest has experienced the driest period in as many as 12,000 years. UCLA climate scientist Park Williams said, "The thing that is really remarkable about this drought period is that temperatures have been warmer than average in all of the years but one."[46] Along with a lack of rainfall, the higher temperatures and low humidity facilitate the evaporation of water from soils and lakes, affecting farms, ranches, and municipal water supplies.

The once great Colorado River, Lake Powell, Lake Mead, and most other rivers and lakes of the Southwest are at record low levels, leaving agricultural enterprises and cities with too little water. As a result, livestock in several western states are being auctioned off or slaughtered because pastures are too dry to support them. For small farmers, soil and water management are keys to success, and the latter is most vulnerable to climate change.

For farmers in Central America, weather extremes are compounded by an increasing number and severity of tropical storms. The National Risk Index, a measure of disaster risk applied to 172 countries worldwide, lists Guatemala and El Salvador as particularly vulnerable to earthquakes, droughts, and hurricanes. A multiyear drought between 2015 and 2017 plagued the Northern Triangle* and led to financial disaster for farmers and to hunger across the region. In 2018, Guatemala and Honduras ranked second and third highest (behind Haiti) in hunger levels across Central America and the Caribbean, as measured by the International Food Policy Research Institute's Global Hunger Index.[47] Many of the desperate people who attempt to immigrate to the United States are fleeing not only extreme violence, but also extreme poverty and hunger. In the absence of effective measures to relieve their plight, the "caravans" of Central Americans heading north will likely only increase in number.

---

* The Northern Triangle of Central America is comprised of the countries of El Salvador, Honduras, and Guatemala.

"A northward shift in where we grow foods commercially is one of the most likely new agricultural frontiers," according to Merritt Turetsky, an ecologist at the University of Colorado Boulder. The long-term prospects of a warming planet will undoubtedly see significant geographic shifts in where some food crops can most productively be grown, or where they will even be viable. Then, the cultivation of previously untouched ecosystems could create their own problems. For example, "we know that drainage of tropical peatlands for palm oil production has released large amounts of stored peat carbon to the atmosphere," Professor Turetsky explained. "As a society, we must protect our northern peatlands and carbon-rich soils from drainage and cultivation."[48]

The ongoing warming of our planet has and will continue to present a growing number of challenges. Public awareness is beginning to reduce emissions, but not nearly enough. Perhaps the powerful forces of free enterprise will develop practical ways to extract greenhouse gases from the atmosphere and, thereby, reduce the likelihood of catastrophe. As we will see in Chapter 8, new technologies offer at least some hope of that. But significant progress certainly cannot be made without the initiative of a motivated populous and its political leaders.

It is incumbent upon each of us to have some understanding of the challenges of growing populations and climate change, and a willingness to do our part in addressing them—to make responsible personal choices and to elect public officials who understand and acknowledge the issues and who are willing to work for the long-term best interests of our world and its children.

6

Are We to Blame?

B efore he was elected president, on November 6, 2012, Donald J. Trump tweeted, "The concept of global warming was created by and for the Chinese in order to make U.S. manufacturing non-competitive." Though he later claimed to be joking, he never really changed his mind about that, even after, as president, government scientists had repeatedly presented him with evidence of global warming, the associated climate change, and the causes.

According to his aides, President Trump didn't actually read the reports because he was confident that he already knew all about that subject. His views about matters of science came from Fox News, much like, as he explained, how he had been informed about matters of foreign policy.[1] Fox News and other right-wing broad-casters are where climate science deniers enjoy plenty of airtime. The hosts have regularly presented scientists from among the three percent of climate scientists or meteorologists who deny human activity has contributed to global warming, or they will present someone with an explanation of how the other 97 percent of scientists have gotten it wrong or are going along with a hoax. Numerous hypotheses have been presented to allegedly explain why scientists "go along." The most prominent among them alleges that scientists do it for the money, particularly research grant money.

Research grants are often awarded by scientific review panels that score the merits of grant proposals submitted by researchers. Bias has sometimes been suspected in the approvals or rejections of grants based on the race of the researchers. Some have alleged that researchers who are skeptical of the consensus regarding the causes of global warming are similarly discriminated against and denied funding. As a result, the theory goes, researchers go along with the consensus in order to get funding. The trouble with that idea is it overlooks a fundamental reality about science and scientists.

Most scientists, like most everyone else in the world, would love to make a name for themselves by discovering something no one else has discovered. So, rather than going along with a consensus, there is every incentive to go against the consensus, the way Copernicus and Galileo changed the traditional understanding of our solar system; or the way Mendel changed traditional ideas about heredity; or the way Crick and Watson furthered our understanding of heredity; or the way Einstein changed consensus thinking about space, time, and gravity. Research scientists are always looking for new ways to understand the world and how it works, and if they can demonstrate that most everyone else has gotten it wrong, they can achieve notoriety.

A consensus is formed after numerous researchers have examined a problem in a number of ways and reached a similar conclusion. There will always be contrarians, as there should be. It is possible to find scientists who proclaim that Earth is flat. But, until they can credibly demonstrate how the rest of us have succumbed to an illusion that it is spherical, they will, as they should, remain on the sidelines.

We can be confident our planet is getting warmer and human activity has significantly contributed to that warming because a great many scientists have examined the issue from many different perspectives and at least 97 percent of them have reached that conclusion. Here is what we know:

We know Earth is getting warmer because it can be measured. It may seem odd to think we can measure our planet's temperature, since it is always different from one location to another, and always changing from day to night and from summer to winter. For this reason, absolute temperature readings are converted to temperature anomalies—the difference between the immediate temperature and the long-term average temperature at each of 6,300 weather stations, research stations, ships, and buoys around the globe[2] at particular dates and times. Also, satellites are used by several government agencies to make similar measurements and calculations.

There are four major data sources for studying global temperatures—the U.K. Met Office Hadley Centre working jointly with the University of East Anglia's Climate Research Unit, the U.S. NASA Goddard Institute for Space Sciences, the U.S. National Oceanic and Atmospheric Administration (NOAA), and the Japan Meteorological Agency. All agree that Earth is getting warmer, and the planet's poles are warming the fastest.

On NOAA's *Climate.gov* website, some of the highlights of that agency's findings are listed:

- Earth's temperature has risen by 0.14° Fahrenheit (0.08° Celsius) per decade since 1880, and the rate of warming over the past 40 years is more than twice that.

- The 10 warmest years on record have occurred since 2005.

- From 1900 to 1980, a new temperature record was set on average every 13.5 years; from 1981 to 2019, a new record was set every 3 years.

- Despite a late-year La Niña event that cooled a wide swath of the tropical Pacific Ocean, 2020 came just 0.04° F (0.02° C) shy of tying 2016 for the warmest year on record. Temperatures over land areas that year experienced record warmth.

- Averaged across land and ocean, the 2020 surface temperature was 1.76° F (0.98° C) warmer than the twentieth-century average of 57.0° F (13.9° C) and 2.14° F (1.19° C) warmer than the pre-industrial period (1880-1900).

 The temperature rises NOAA describes may not seem like much. But, as we have seen, small temperature rises have already had significant effects. Furthermore, the numbers described above are global averages, while some specific locales have seen significantly higher temperature rises, along with consequential changes in local climates. The poles, for example, are warming faster and the Arctic is warming the fastest, resulting in the loss of ice and affecting the entire planet. The loss of sea ice is even more directly affecting the survivability of several species that depend on it, ultimately affecting the interconnected ecosystems of all the world's oceans.

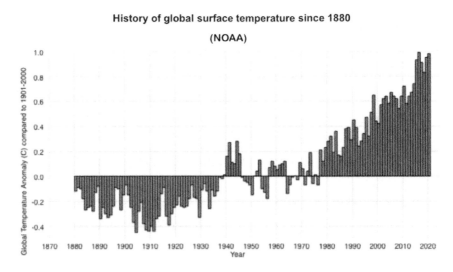

History of global surface temperature since 1880

(NOAA)

An important thing to notice about the numbers above is that the warming is accelerating. According to NASA, the glaciers of Greenland and Antarctica are now melting six times faster than they were in the 1990s.[3]

A 2021 report by the World Meteorological Organization (an agency of the United Nations) warned temperatures are rising faster than previously predicted. The report said there is a good chance that at least one of the next five years will reach a temperature of 1.5° Celsius above the temperatures of the late 1800s, and that multi-year averages will soon reach that amount. Randall Cerveny, a climate scientist at Arizona State University and a World Meteorological Organization rapporteur who was not involved in the report, said, "[1.5° Celsius] is a very, very, very, big number. We need to be concerned about it."[4]

The 2015 Paris Climate Accord* had set a goal of limiting the average global temperature rise to 2° Celsius by the end of the century and, ideally, keeping it below a 1.5° Celsius increase. Yet, the United Nations has now warned that, if emissions are not significantly abated, we are on track for more than a 3° Celsius (5.4° Fahrenheit) increase by the end of the century. That is a very big deal!

Some people may ask, "how much could human activity be the cause of global warming and the accompanying climate change?" Plenty.

The first thing to think about is that the "greenhouse effect" we hear so much about is a good thing—a really good thing. Without it, we wouldn't be here.

Ozone (O_3) and other gases in the atmosphere help to reflect some of the sun's harmful UV light away from the surface of the Earth, making terrestrial life possible. Even more important, however, is the greenhouse effect, where water vapor and other gases in the atmosphere trap the heat of the sun and hold it close to Earth's

---

* The Paris Climate Accord only set goals. It provided no enforcement mechanisms.

surface, moderating temperature fluctuations and generally keeping the earth warm. Without the atmosphere and those greenhouse gases within it, Earth's surface temperatures would be much hotter during the day and extremely cold at night, much like the moon or Mars. Earth would be inhospitable to life.

Water vapor is the most abundant of the greenhouse gases, accounting for about 60 percent of the warming effect of all such gases. Furthermore, more water vapor in the atmosphere is a result of a warmer planet. Warmer temperatures enable the atmosphere to hold more water vapor, and warmer seawater facilitates more humidity. The effect is reversed when clouds reflect sunlight back into space. But on balance, there is a feedback loop, where more water vapor brings more warming, which brings more water vapor, which brings more warming, which...

Humans don't do very much to directly put water vapor into the atmosphere, but the gases that we do put into it significantly amplify the warming effects of water vapor.

Andrew Dessler, who has studied the issue along with his colleagues at Texas A&M University, said "dumping greenhouse gases into the atmosphere makes the atmosphere more humid. And since water vapor is itself a greenhouse gas, the increase in humidity amplifies the warming from carbon dioxide. ... We now think the water vapor feedback is extraordinarily strong, capable of doubling the warming due to carbon dioxide alone."[5]

Like water vapor, other greenhouses gases, such as carbon dioxide, methane, nitrous oxide, and ozone, occur naturally in the atmosphere. A sixth group of very potent greenhouse gases—chlorofluorocarbons—do not. They are man-made. Most significantly, all of those gases, aside from water vapor, are directly released into the atmosphere by human activity at rates that far exceed their natural occurrence. Therefore, we can have some control of the amount of these gases in the atmosphere, if we will.

Here is a description of how the major greenhouse gases are emitted by human activity, as described by the U.S. Environmental Protection Agency (EPA):

- **Carbon dioxide (CO_2)** enters the atmosphere through the burning of fossil fuels (such as coal, natural gas, and oil), solid waste, trees, and other biological materials. It is also produced by certain chemical reactions, such as in the manufacture of cement.

- **Methane (CH_4)** is emitted during the production and transport of coal, natural gas, and oil. Methane emissions also result from livestock and other agricultural practices and land use, and by the decay of organic waste in municipal solid waste landfills.

- **Nitrous oxide (N_2O)** is emitted with agricultural practices and other industrial activities, land use, the combustion of fossil fuels and solid waste, as well as with wastewater treatment.

- **Fluorinated gases**, such as **hydrofluorocarbons, perfluoro-carbons, sulfur hexafluoride**, and **nitrogen trifluoride** are synthetic, powerful greenhouse gases that are emitted from a variety of industrial processes. Fluorinated gases are some-times used as substitutes for stratospheric, **ozone-depleting** sub-stances, such as **chlorofluorocarbons, hydrochloro-fluorocarbons**, and **halons**. These gases are typically emitted in smaller quantities, but because they are potent greenhouse gases, they are sometimes referred to as High Global Warming Potential gases.[6]

In the atmosphere, visible sunlight (*shortwave* radiation) easily passes through these gases and water vapor, and that which is not reflected back into space by clouds reaches and heats the earth's surface. The heat energy that radiates from the earth's surface (or any object) is *longwave* radiation. The longwave radiation warms the lower atmosphere, but does not readily pass through the greenhouse gases back into space. Just like the glass or plastic of a garden greenhouse allows light to come through, but traps most of the heat inside, greenhouse gases block much of the heat from escaping the lower atmosphere. (Hence the name.)

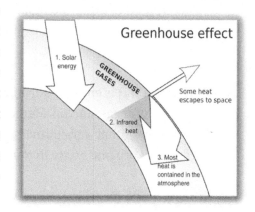

Scientists know quite a lot about the fluctuations of global temperatures over the history of the earth. Geological and paleontological evidence reveals the occurrences of ice ages and the melting and refreezing of the poles. Ice core samples taken at the poles, particularly Antarctica, also reveal historic temperature variations through analyses of the ratios of "light" oxygen-16 to "heavy" oxygen-18 at various depths of the cores.[7] Those ice cores also contain air bubbles that are tiny samples of the atmosphere at various times going back as far 800,000 years. So, the amounts of CO_2 in the atmosphere over the years can be paired with global temperatures to see correlations.

The ice core samples reveal a correlation between higher CO_2 levels and higher temperatures. It appears, however, that the higher CO_2 levels tend to follow the warmer temperatures, rather than what we would expect if higher CO_2 levels were a contributing cause of the warming. Edward Brook of Oregon State University's College of Earth, Ocean and Atmospheric Sciences explained, "The idea that there was a lag of CO_2 behind temperature is something climate change skeptics pick on." Researchers at the Laboratory of Glaciology and Geophysical Environment in France have discovered, however, that the way the air diffuses through the ice over many years of compaction makes the air bubbles much younger than the ice surrounding them, largely negating the contradiction.[8]

These samples of our planet's atmosphere also tell us that the level of greenhouse gases is higher now than at any other time in the last 800,000 years. And the levels are continuing to rise, as human activity is injecting about 40 billion metric tons of CO_2 into the atmosphere each year.

Atmospheric carbon dioxide breaks down after about 100 years, and the world's forests, particularly tropical rain forests and wetlands, as well as all other vegetation, absorb CO_2 and emit oxygen. But emissions of CO_2 from human activities are far exceeding what nature removes.

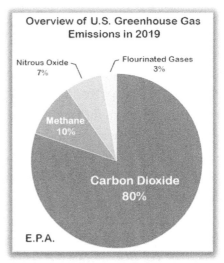

During the growing seasons of late spring and summer in each of the Southern and Northern Hemispheres, the world's plants absorb CO_2 from the atmosphere. Conversely, each fall, winter, and early spring, the world's plants and soil emit CO_2, contributing to the rise of global levels. Since there is more land mass in the Northern Hemisphere, the month of May typically sees the highest concentrations of CO_2 each year.

In May of 2021, NOAA measured the highest concentration of CO_2 in the atmosphere the agency has ever recorded since it began measurements in 1958 at the Mauna Loa Observatory in Hawaii. That record came despite the previous 15 months of significantly less human activity and lower emissions due to the COVID-19 pandemic. As a result of the pandemic, 2020 saw a nearly 4 percent decrease in demand for energy, resulting in a 5.8 percent reduction of CO_2 emissions, according to the International Energy Agency. It was the largest annual decline in at least 75 years, but it was not enough to arrest the rise of concentrations of CO_2 in our atmosphere.[9]

Pieter Tans, a senior scientist at NOAA's Global Monitoring Laboratory, explained in an interview, "It's not significant in the sense that we are surprised. It was fully expected. It's significant in that it shows we are still fully on the wrong track."[10]

The political climate is changing, and many industries, even energy companies, are adapting. There is hope. There are solutions being imagined, as we will see in Chapter 8. But there remain plenty of politicians and members of the general public around the world who fail to recognize the urgency of the problem, and who are inhibiting meaningful progress. All the while, massive greenhouse gas emissions continue.

Political feasibility has limited the agreements that have been reached so far, and most countries are failing to live up to the modest commitments they have already made. So, there is much more to do. The more greenhouses gases we put in the atmosphere, the more difficult it will be to avert disaster. As Dr. Tans put it, "The goals so far are themselves insufficient, even after having been beefed up. We're running out of time. The longer we wait, the harder it gets."[11]

In his prophetic book, *Earth in the Balance*, some three decades ago, Senator Al Gore of Tennessee warned Earth's natural resources were being overtaxed and carbon dioxide and other greenhouse gas emissions were causing global warming. Having studied environmental issues in his work, first as a U.S. Congressman and then as a U.S. Senator, Gore well understood the most pressing environmental challenges facing the world at that time. He also cited reasons for optimism—optimism if the forces of political power in the United States and the world could step up to meet those challenges.

For his efforts, Gore's political opposition, particularly as he ran for the vice presidency, offered scathing rebukes and ridicule. They said that the stated threats were overblown and that the suggested remedies would ruin the economy. Many of the same voices continue to express skepticism of human activity affecting climate change or dismiss its significance.

It was evident to many people at the time of his book's publication that Gore's political opposition had gotten it wrong on both counts. But thirty more years of environmental and economic studies have made it even more clear that there is plenty to be concerned about, that humans have played a significant role in contributing to climate change, and that the economic costs of doing nothing far exceed those of mitigation.

An August 9, 2021 report by the United Nations Intergovernmental Panel on Climate Change (IPCC) provided the latest evidence that Vice President Gore's warnings were well founded. UN Secretary General António Guterres called the report's findings, "a code red for humanity," adding, "There is no time for delay and no room for excuses."

The landmark and multifaceted report was compiled by 234 authors relying on 14,000 studies from around the world. The report explained that atmospheric CO_2 levels had risen to a level not seen in two million years, and that the levels had not changed so rapidly in 66 million years.

The report went on to explain that if global temperatures were to rise more than two degrees Celsius above preindustrial levels—a near certainty at the current rate of emissions—then a collapse of the Greenland ice sheet would likely inundate coastal communities with six feet of sea-level rise, and many of the world's coral reefs could also be lost.[12]

The IPCC vice chair and a senior advisor to NOAA, Ko Barrett, said, "Unless we make immediate, rapid and large-scale reductions in greenhouse gas emissions, limiting warming to 1.5 degrees Centigrade [the goal set by the Paris Climate Accord] will be beyond reach." She went on to add, "Each bit of warming will intensify the impacts we will likely see."[13]

The report explained that, even if we were to halt emissions today, the cascading effects of what is already in the atmosphere will subject the world to worsening climate impacts for another thirty years. We can expect more frequent and more severe heatwaves, fires, and tropical storms in the years ahead, and the acidity of the world's oceans will continue to increase.

If emissions were aggressively reduced starting today, it may be possible that increases in global temperatures would level off by 2050. As U.S. Special Envoy for Climate John Kerry said, "What the world requires now is action. We can go to the low carbon economy we urgently need, but time is not on our side."[14]

As a result of increasingly sophisticated computer models, researchers are now able to more confidently ascribe man-made climate change as contributing to natural disasters like Houston's 2017 Hurricane Harvey that resulted in unprecedented flooding and 68 deaths, or Mozambique's 2015 Tropical Cyclone Idai, a storm that killed nearly 1,300 people.

As more and more people are impacted, more people are recognizing the world is changing. Climate scientist at the University of East Anglia and a contributor to the report, Corinne Le Quéré observed, "It's now become quite obvious to people what is happening, because we see it with our own eyes."

The IPCC Report declared that, while the role of humans in affecting climate change was once up for debate, the evidence we now have is "overwhelming." What was once hypothesis, is now an "established fact."

7

An Age of Unreason

T he polar vortexes are domes of low pressure and very cold air
in the atmosphere 15 to 30 miles above Earth's North and
South poles. The term "vortex" is derived from the airflow pattern
(counterclockwise over the North, clockwise over the South) that
keeps the air close to the poles.

In the Northern Hemisphere winter, the usually circular
vortex sometimes becomes misshapen and begins to "wobble." It
then expands southward into the jet stream that brings it into the
lower United States, Europe, and/or China, affecting otherwise
normal winter weather patterns. While this phenomenon is known
to have occurred for many years, it has become more frequent and
more pronounced in recent years. Most climatologists attribute the
increasing severity of these events to the warming of the planet,
particularly at the poles.

In February of 2021, the Northern polar vortex was pushed
out of its normal pattern and swept down across the southern
United States, all the way into the entire state of Texas. The result
was temperatures in Texas that were significantly lower than in
Alaska, Greenland, and Norway.[1]

Prolonged record low temperatures across Texas that
February overwhelmed the electric power grid, causing multiday
blackouts for some 4.5 million residents.[2] Water service also was
interrupted in many areas, including the entire Houston municipal

water supply that serves about 2.2 million people. The event took the lives of at least 246 people[3] in a state that is unaccustomed to such extremely cold temperatures.

In his first public statement regarding the event, Texas Governor Greg Abbott explained how the extreme cold had crippled all sources of electricity generation. Abbott tweeted, "This includes the natural gas & coal generators." As University of Texas Energy Resources Professor Michael Webber noted, coal piles and equipment had frozen at coal-fired power plants; pumps had frozen at a nuclear power plant; several natural gas plants' equipment had frozen and compressors that ensure the flow of gas to the plants had shut down; a large percentage of wind turbines were hampered by ice on the blades; and some solar panels were covered by snow.[4]

When Governor Abbott appeared on Fox News the following day, however, his story changed. It evidently changed in order to fit a disinformation narrative about the event that was emerging on Fox News, Newsmax, Breitbart, and other media platforms of the political Right. In an interview with Sean Hannity, Abbott blamed the grid failure on renewable energy sources, proclaiming, "This shows how the Green New Deal would be a deadly deal for the United States of America." Abbott went on to say, "It just shows that fossil fuel is necessary for the state of Texas, as well as other states, to make sure that we will be able to heat our homes in the wintertime and cool our homes in the summertime."

The previous summer, several Texas Republicans had blamed power outages in California on that state's efforts to use more clean, renewable energy. In August 2020, Texas Lt. Governor Dan Patrick tweeted, "This is what happens when Democrats are left in charge. Why California's liberal climate policies are causing electricity blackouts." Senator Ted Cruz tweeted, "Biden/Harris-/AOC want to make CA's failed energy policy the standard nationwide. Hope you don't like air conditioning!" In September, Texas Attorney General Ken Paxton tweeted, "California's politicians did this, not the heat."[5]

These Texas politicians' attempts to ridicule and demonize clean, renewable energy sources and their proponents is, in part, an effort to defend the fossil fuel industry for which Texas is well known. But it is something more than that. It is also part of a more general aversion to science that has arisen among recent Republican Party officeholders and a great many of their constituents—an antipathy that has reached into several realms of scientific knowledge and discovery, including biological evolutionary science, climate science, sociology and, most recently, immunology.

Of course, it is not only the political Right who sometimes reject the findings of science, as we will see momentarily. But, in recent decades, it has become undeniably more common among Republicans and the political Right. Furthermore, in a few short years, truthfulness has become even less valued among politicians than it once was. Since Governor Abbott had told the truth in an earlier tweet, we can only conclude that he intentionally or impulsively lied about the causes of the power failures when speaking to his desired base constituency on Fox News.

A rather boorish political culture has arisen that not only rejects science, but devalues truthfulness in a variety of spheres. In many respects, for a large portion of our society, we are living in an unscientific, post-truth world—an *age of unreason*. So, how did we get here?

For many centuries after the Dark Ages in Western culture, the realms of scientific and theological discovery worked hand in hand. Intellectuals sought to understand God's work using two books—the book of Scripture and the book of Nature. In fact, many of human-kind's most important scientific discoveries were the work of monks, clergy, and religious scholars.

Nicolaus Copernicus (1473-1543), the man most credited with discovering our heliocentric solar system, was Canon at Frombork Cathedral (in what is now northern Poland). An Italian Jesuit priest named Francesco Grimaldi (1618-1663) was first to accurately describe the characteristics of light diffraction and, in fact, coined the term "diffraction." An Austrian monk named Gregory Mendel (1822-1884) discovered the principles of genetics and is today known as the "father of genetics." An Italian Catholic priest named Antonio Stoppani (1824-1891), also a geologist and paleontologist, was among the first to propose a geological epoch defined by the human activities that had altered the character of the landscape. There are many, many others. And yet, science and religion are commonly, and erroneously, thought to be incompatible. The perceived conflicts have been the result, not of genuine incompatibilities of science and religion, but of failures to comprehend sound theological principles.

One of the first and perhaps the most famous of these conflicts arose when Galileo Galilei's observations prompted him to endorse the Copernican view of a heliocentric solar system. In 1616, the Catholic Church had declared Earth was at the center of the universe and any different idea was heretical. (Protestants also objected to any idea that contradicted a geocentric universe.) So, when Galileo's observations became publicly known, he was infamously subjected to an Inquisition trial for the crime of heresy.

We now know the Church got it wrong. It was not the Bible that got it wrong.[6] It was ecclesiastic authorities who failed to adequately understand Scripture. And it wouldn't be the last time men of limited imaginations would misinterpret and misuse the Bible.

Though the scientific method can be traced back to antiquity, its importance was newly recognized through the work of Copernicus, Galileo, Francis Bacon, Johannes Kepler, Rene Descartes, Isaac Newton, and others, from the 16th to the 18th centuries. From the 12th century until the end of the 17th century, scholasticism dominated the curriculum in most European universities. Scholasticism was a theistic philosophy that emphasized tradition and religious dogma, where the product of all inquiry had to fit into the preconceived conclusions of religious authorities. The scientific method, on the other hand, begins with objective observation and draws conclusions only when hypotheses can be tested for their veracity, regardless of where the findings might lead.

To this day, resistance to science is most often founded upon preconceived preferences that run counter to its findings. That has been a significant portion of the objections to the findings of biological evolutionary science. Some people simply cannot stomach the idea that we share a common ancestor with apes, much less every other living creature on Earth. A 2004 book titled *Uncommon Dissent: Intellectuals Who Find Darwinism Unconvincing*, contained essays from sixteen of the world's leading Intelligent Design* proponents. Only four of the sixteen were biologists. The primary focus of the text was the contributors' explanations of why they believed evolution *should not* be real, rather than why they believed it *is not* real.

Of course, many people also believe evolution is contradicted by the Bible. But, just as when the Church insisted that Earth was stationary and at the center of the universe, that idea is born of a misunderstanding of Scripture and, more significantly, an unduly shallow understanding of the concept of God.

Skepticism of science has also been exacerbated by the distortion or misapplication of its findings. When Charles Darwin published *On the Origin of Species*, the concept of natural selection was soon misapplied to sociology. In fact, the phrase, "survival of the fittest" did not originate with Darwin. The phrase was coined by an English philosopher of sociology named Herbert Spencer, who drew parallels between Darwin's discoveries in biology and his own sociological evolutionary theories that had been published six years earlier.

Spencer argued that the struggle of human populations for subsistence had led to the improvement of the human condition, as

---

* "Intelligent Design" is a theory that proclaims evolution could only have occurred with the supernatural intervention of an Intelligent Designer. The movement is a spin-off of "creation science," which religious conservatives had sought to have taught in public school science classes, but were rebuffed by the courts because it is religious instruction, not science.

individuals of superior intellect, skill, ingenuity, and self-control had adapted through technological innovation. Less capable populations or individuals had simply perished or were subjugated. Spencer formulated a theory that would later come to be called "Social Darwinism," even though it had nothing to do with Charles Darwin or his work—nothing to do the mechanism that Darwin had discovered for how biological evolution works.

Because of his belief in the natural evolution of human progress, Spencer promoted an ultra-conservative political philosophy that emphasized the rights and freedom of individuals at the exclusion of collective initiatives. He opposed all government aid to the poor because he believed them to be inferior and unfit. He wrote, "The whole effort of nature is to get rid of such, to clear the world of them, and make room for better."[7] His views were well received among the political Right in England and in the United States, and helped to justify the promotion of laissez-faire economics, imperialism, fascism, and racist ideologies and practices like eugenics. Spencer and his followers simply ignored the fact that a great many species survive and prosper as a result of interspecies cooperation and even altruism.

A similar distortion of science occurred soon after Albert Einstein's theories of Special Relativity and General Relativity became widely publicized. Much like Darwin's work, Einstein's theories became misrepresented and erroneously applied to sociology, ethics, and art. As historian Paul Johnson lamented,

> At the beginning of the 1920s the belief began to circulate, for the first time at a popular level, that there were no longer any absolutes: of time and space, of good and evil, of knowledge, above all of value. Mistakenly but perhaps inevitably, relativity became confused with relativism.[8]

Most people didn't really understand Einstein's theories, particularly the math. Nevertheless, the idea that motion, space, and time were not firmly fixed, but were instead relative to any number of perspectives, excited the imagination. Artists and philosophers were drawn to what they saw as romantic notions that could be applied outside of the specific physics of Einstein's calculations. In his 1923 book, *The Modern Theme*, Spanish humanist philosopher José Ortega y Gasset proclaimed,

> The theory of Einstein is a marvelous proof of the harmonious multiplicity of all points of view. If the idea is extended to morals and aesthetics, we shall come to experience history and life in a new way.[9]

Art critics began to declare that the transition from classical to modern art could be traced to a transition from Newtonian physics to Einsteinian ideas about space and time. Art historian Paul LaPorte declared that, "the new pictorial idiom created by Cubism is most satisfactorily explained by applying it to the concept of the space-time continuum."

Einstein was annoyed at such comparisons, explaining that, "This new artistic 'language' has nothing in common with the Theory of Relativity."[10] Of course, nor does the language of moral relativism.

Though they are often used in efforts to discredit science, it should be well understood that proclamations of Moral Relativism or Social Darwinism have no basis in the science they seek to incorporate.

The 1950s saw new reasons for people to be fearful or skeptical of science. While science had helped Allied Forces to win World War II with things like radar and atomic weapons, the Cold War in an atomic age brought fears of annihilation and, with it, a degree of pessimistic fatalism. The horror of what atomic bombs had done to Hiroshima and Nagasaki and the development of the far more powerful hydrogen bomb* created the idea that science had become

---

* A hydrogen bomb is as much as 1,000 times more powerful than the atomic bombs used on Hiroshima and Nagasaki.

wholly removed from ethical constraint. As American General Omar Bradley lamented in his 1948 Armistice Day speech,

> Our knowledge of science has clearly outstripped our capacity to control it. We have many men of science, but too few men of God. We grasped the mystery of the atom and rejected the Sermon on the Mount. Man is stumbling blindly through a spiritual darkness while toying with the precarious secrets of life and death. The world has achieved brilliance without wisdom, power without conscience. Ours is a world of nuclear giants and ethical infants.[11]

Governments have long used science in the development of weapons, as well as other initiatives that directly benefit the well-being of the state (like geographic exploration, for example). While medical research and "pure science" (that which seeks knowledge without an immediate application) have more often been undertaken by universities, independent inventors, and entrepreneurs. But, after World War II, President Roosevelt wanted the United States to extend its wartime science initiatives for reasons of national security, to combat disease, and to promote the scientific talent of the nation's youth. Consequently, under President Truman, the National Science Foundation was created. Medical research and pure science have been largely driven by government investments ever since, and can thus be conflated with military spending.

After the Soviet Union detonated its own atomic bomb in August 1949, the "arms race" was on. Throughout the 1950s, both the Soviet Union and the United States endeavored to develop more powerful bombs. They invented more capable missiles, aircraft, and naval vessels for the delivery of those bombs. They developed new classes of nuclear-powered ships and submarines. They developed better tanks, war planes, and attack helicopters. They developed and launched spy satellites, and much more.

By the end of the decade, President Eisenhower had become alarmed by what he termed the "military industrial complex." The profit motives of defense contractors had become a powerful force in military decision making. The so-called "missile gap" that John F. Kennedy spoke of in 1958 was, at least in part, the invention of the public relations and lobbying arms of the missile manufacturers. A "bomber gap" a few years earlier had also been a business-interest illusion. In reality, the Soviet Union never had a military capability that was comparable to the United States (except, perhaps, in heavy rockets).

By the 1960s, it was also becoming known that science and new technologies were poisoning the environment. Rachel Carson's widely read 1962 book, *Silent Spring*, illustrated how the use and the overuse of chemical pesticides were negatively affecting human health by direct exposure and by polluting water sources. Pesticides were also killing more than their intended targets and thereby damaging crucial ecosystems. Even America's national symbol, the bald eagle, was on the verge of extinction.

As the Viet Nam War dragged on with its use of Agent Orange and napalm, its futility became increasingly obvious and opened a divide between the Greatest Generation, who had followed their government's lead out of the Great Depression and through World War II, and their children—the "baby-boom" generation—who grew up, despite unprecedented prosperity, with the fear of nuclear war and the draft, and a feeling of powerlessness against "the establishment" (government, science, and big business) that they saw as the instigators of senseless wars, pollution, and depraved materialism. The result has been an anti-government, anti-science sentiment that has stayed, whether consciously or subconsciously, with many people of the baby-boom generation. (Though the aversion to materialism portion of that equation appears to have fully waned.)

That fatalistic sentiment was put on hold, however, with the Apollo 11 mission that put three Americans on the surface of the Moon. It was a time of national pride—indeed, the pride of the world.

It was a magnificent accomplishment resulting from a partnership of government and science. Numerous technologies that spun off of that effort have improved all of our lives.

Manned space exploration has excited the imagination ever since. It is manned space flight that can garner the political support needed to fund space exploration. This is unfortunate because there is very little that can be learned or accomplished with manned missions that cannot be done with automation at far less expense. The recent discussion of sending astronauts to Mars, for example, is more about public relations and politics than about science.

Despite the enthusiasm and the collateral benefits of the Moon landing, some people complained about its costs, suggesting that the money should have been spent to help the poor. Nevertheless, most people likely believe that pure science has value. Undoubtedly, everyone can appreciate the development of microwave ovens, personal computers, and cell phones. But, however subtle it may be, an underlying suspicion of science lingers, and an increasingly complicated world has made many of us even more vulnerable to misinformation.

After having been upheld by an 8 to 0 vote in the United States Supreme Court in 1969, the Fairness Doctrine was abolished by the Federal Communications Commission (FCC) by a 4 to 0 vote during the Ronald Reagan Administration. The doctrine had been enacted in 1949 to require radio and television broadcasters to devote airtime to matters of public interest and to include opposing views whenever available. The rule was meant to ensure audiences would be exposed to a diversity of views so they could make informed judgments.

The Fairness Doctrine was only a rule, so it could be eliminated by a vote of the political appointees of the FCC. After that happened in 1987, Congress attempted to convert the doctrine into law, but President Reagan vetoed the legislation.[12]

The most famous beneficiary of the repeal was Rush Limbaugh, a radio DJ-turned-political-shock-jock, who began to take advantage of the new guidelines immediately. His radio show was then nationally syndicated in 1988 and would eventually be carried on over 650 radio stations nationwide. Many others, mostly on the political Right, followed.

Proponents of the repeal of the Fairness Doctrine argued that a free marketplace of ideas would result in the best ideas, much like the competition of free enterprise results in the best products. In practice, however, it hasn't worked like that. Shawn Otto, the author of the 2016 book *The War on Science*, aptly observed,

> Diversity of thought has been quashed in favor of an uncritical, authoritarian, and vehemently partisan allegiance to a political tribe—a new conservative identity politics that rejects the left-wing identity politics of the postmodern era. The talk jocks as chorus masters, conducting the audience members' political opinions in an us-versus-them narrative that maximizes audience share and directs the anger and political contributions of millions of listeners like so many sports fans.[13]

It should be remembered that Rush Limbaugh fans happily referred to themselves as "dittoheads," as they abandoned critical thinking and looked to a cheerleader for their worst instincts.

To better illustrate the attraction of Limbaugh's rhetoric, Otto pointed to two personality types that have been defined by educators, one of which is more drawn to narratives provided by right-wing broadcast outlets.

> To better understand the effect of the Fairness Doctrine's repeal, consider a bit of educational psychology: the cognitive style of "field-dependent" and "field-independent" personalities. Field-dependent personalities are more socially oriented and require externally defined

goals and reinforcements. Field-independent personal-ities are more analytical and tend to have self-defined goals and reinforcements. Educators have developed strategies for teaching people with each learning style. Field-dependent citizens in the population, who valued authority and looked for guidance, needed the protection of the Fairness Doctrine to give them a fair grasp of reality. In the doctrine's absence, many field-dependent people have drifted under the influence of slanted conservative commercial media, creating one of the most divided political climates in history.

Otto went on to add:

> ... By freeing broadcasters from the requirement of fair-ness and thus the need to ground their messages in established knowledge and fact, the repeal plummeted the country into a partisan public dialogue. One-sided rhetor-ical arguments backed by outrage and wattage could now hold sway over facts and reason.

Similarly, psychologists describe what they call "authori-tarian" personalities. People with authoritarian personality traits are more likely to call themselves "patriots," as they are drawn to the idea of belonging to a traditional authoritative structure and a group identity. They are attracted to strong leaders with simple or well-defined messages. With a strictly delineated group identity (whether by race, religion, political party, or nationality, for example), authori-tarians are often intolerant of outsiders and have tendencies of scapegoating. They tend to see the world in simplistic notions of right and wrong or good and evil or loyal or disloyal to their group identity, with little appreciation for nuance or varying perspectives. Consequently, most people with authoritarian personality tenden-cies subscribe to a "conservative" political identity.

So, a radio personality like Rush Limbaugh who can artfully reinforce a tribal identity, while blaming the world's problems on others can be quite attractive to a significant portion of the population. Naturally, television personalities who offer that same appeal can also draw large audiences.

In 1996, Australian tabloid publishing magnate Rupert Murdoch teamed up with former Republican Party strategist Roger Ailes to create a new 24-hour news network. Fox News used sound effects and bold graphics to set itself apart from competitors. In coverage of the September 11, 2001 attacks, Fox was the first network to run a "news ticker" on the bottom of the screen to deliver additional information about fast-breaking events. Most significantly, Fox News provided the platform that Ailes had long sought for the dissemination of politically conservative views.

While the hard news division of Fox has remained credible in some respects (as exhibited by the Fox News Headlines on Sirius XM Radio)[14], the overall tint of the network (and particularly its prime-time programming) has effectively become a mouthpiece and propaganda arm of the political Right and the Republican Party. Without the Fairness Doctrine, there has been no check on opinion and propaganda posing as news. The result has been an even more extreme political division among the American people, and a proliferation of misinformation and misconception.

After supporters of President Trump stormed the U.S. Capitol on January 6, 2021, former Australian Prime Minister Malcolm Turnbull, who had personally known Murdoch and his family for 45 years, accused him and Fox News of undermining democracy, noting that News Corp outlets like Fox were, "utterly liberated from the truth."

> What does Vladimir Putin want to do with his operations in America? He wants to divide America and turn Americans against each other. That is exactly what Murdoch has done: divided Americans against each other and so undermined their faith in political institutions that

a mob of thousands of people, many of them armed, stormed the Capitol.[15]

When President Trump claimed the 2020 election had been stolen from him, Fox News broadcasted false and slanderous propaganda in an effort to support his claim. Allegations by the network and individuals who appeared on the network, as well as other right-wing media outlets, were so demonstrably false that the network and many of those individuals became vulnerable to lawsuits from two voting machine companies that had been the subjects of their allegations of election fraud.

In appearances on Fox and other right-wing media outlets, attorney Sidney Powell proclaimed the 2020 presidential election was stolen from Trump by Dominion voting machines that had been built to rig elections for Venezuelan strongman Hugo Chavez. When sued by Dominion, her defense posited, "No reasonable person would conclude that the statements were truly statements of fact."[16] Yet, a great many people did.

A December 2020 Quinnipiac University poll revealed that 77 percent of self-identified Republicans and 35 percent of independents believed the claims of a stolen election.[17] This was despite the fact that the only evidence of fraud were the unsupported claims made by Trump, his attorneys, and a few members of his staff and members of Congress—after the Republican local officials who had actually run the election and Trump's own Director of Cyber Security had said it was "the most secure in American history."[18]

Most troubling (and revealing of human nature) is how one man's con could garner so many accomplices and fool so many people. P.T. Barnum once said, "The common man, no matter how sharp and tough, actually enjoys having the wool pulled over his eyes." As a result of Dominion Voting System's defamation case against Fox, we learned from internal memos that Barnum's aphorism aligns well with the Fox News business model. The on-air hosts and top executives alike understood that Trump's claim was a lie, but they promoted it anyway because they believed their audience preferred to be told that particular lie, instead of being informed of the truth. Fox feared a loss of viewers.

We can see a similar dynamic with other subjects, including climate change. People on the political Right tend to be skeptical of climate change because of an impression that its mitigation could be an imposition. Therefore, they are drawn to narratives suggesting the problem is overblown or even an invention of the Left. Because there is profit in it, Fox News and other right-wing media outlets, as well as quite a few successful books, provide those narratives. They also stoke fear with disinformation, like suggesting our SUVs and gas stoves will be taken from us, for example. Truthful news and public service are sacrificed for profit.

Thus, the issue of climate change has been politicized and skepticism has become a part of the Fox News culture—a partisan political culture where, like in all political cultures, loyalty to the group and the defense of its leaders can escape the bounds of rational thought and behavior.

It is important to recognize that our vulnerability to the pernicious effects of partisanship and disinformation usually has less to do with intellect than with emotion. Very smart people can have a need to align with a faction or an ideology and thereby succumb to the deceptions that may come with them. Furthermore, once aligned with a faction and its disinformation, pride, emotion, and tribal thinking can inhibit enlightenment, regardless of any amount of contradicting information. As Jonathon Swift observed long ago, "Reasoning will never make a man correct an ill opinion, which by reasoning he never acquired."

Along with the Trump presidency came a time when telling the truth was increasingly optional for politicians and television personalities alike. Events also revealed that a great many people are vulnerable to believing, not just illogical claims, but even the most bizarre conspiracy theories.

Trump and his partisan media enablers sought to discredit traditional news sources and to propagate the notion that a "Deep State" (a secret cabal within the government) was working against him. Some people went so far as to believe that a mysterious high-level intelligence officer dubbed "QAnon" was sending veiled messages on social media about Trump's efforts to thwart that Deep State—for QAnon followers, it was a cabal of Satan-worshipping, child-eating pedophiles like Barack Obama, Hillary Clinton, George Soros, and other Democrats. We can only imagine how Russian Intelligence, or whoever else might have been behind QAnon, were themselves astonished at how gullible people can be.

Of course, there have been whacky conspiracy theories as long as there have been people to dream them up, even before the internet. Many of us remember the "Paul is dead" phenomenon, where it was believed Paul McCartney had died in a car accident and was then replaced with a look-alike. Clues to the conspiracy could be found in Beatles' songs and album covers. Then there were the many Elvis sightings after people had theorized that Elvis Presley's death had been faked. The assassination of President John Kennedy was variously believed to have been the work of the C.I.A., the Mafia, Vice President Lyndon Johnson, or the KGB.

Before becoming child-eating pedophiles, Bill and Hillary Clinton were believed to have murdered Deputy White House Counsel Vince Foster in an effort to cover up their alleged criminal activities. This theory gained a wider following when preacher and conservative moralist Jerry Falwell subsidized and promoted a 1994 film called *The Clinton Chronicles*. The film featured various claims by Christopher Ruddy (a New York Post reporter at the time), including the idea that Foster's gun had been placed in his hand post-mortem. In reality, numerous forensic investigations concluded Foster had committed suicide.

Ruddy would go on to create the ultra-conservative Newsmax website, magazine, and cable news channel—alternatives for those who find Fox News to be too closely aligned with reality. Consumers can find any number of preferred realities, or what Trump advisor Kellyanne Conway called "alternative facts," on websites, blogs, and broadcast outlets like Fox, Newsmax, Breitbart News, OANN (One America News Network), Drudge Report, The

Daily Wire, and a plethora of Talk Radio programs on the Right. On the Left, there are MSNBC, Mother Jones Politics, CNN (often), Daily Kos, Talking Points Memo, and a few others.

Perhaps the most obvious effort to invent new and favored realities was the creation of "Conservapedia," an online encyclopedia designed as an alternative to what it claims is a liberal bias in Wikipedia content. The site proclaims its support for an "American conservative and fundamentalist Christian" worldview.

Launched in 2006 by Andrew Schlafly, the son of Christian conservative activist Phyllis Schlafly, the site presents wild conspiracy theories and political propaganda as fact. Conservapedia articles regularly contradict well-established science. For example, it proclaims, "Climate change is the new name used by liberals for their global warming hoax;" "abortion causes an increase in breast cancer;" and "The theory of relativity is disproved by counterexamples, but is promoted by liberals who like its encouragement of relativism and its tendency to pull people away from the Bible."[19] The mere existence of a site like Conservapedia well illustrates how cultural preferences leave many of us vulnerable to disinformation.

Along with the development of the internet and its many social media platforms, like Facebook, YouTube, Twitter, Instagram, Tumblr, Reddit, Pinterest, Vine, Gab, and Tik Tok, came a plethora of new conspiracy theories. The 9/11/2001 attacks on the World Trade Center and Pentagon were an inside job. Black helicopters were part of a scheme that would bring the U.S. under the control of the United Nations. Barack Obama was born in Kenya and was, thereby, not eligible to be president. The Sandy Hook Elementary School massacre was either a "false flag" operation designed to increase public sentiment for gun control, or did not happen at all. Marjorie Taylor Greene, who had promoted the QAnon theory and had alleged that school shootings were staged, was elected to the United States Congress in 2020, suggesting a significant portion of the American electorate is either tolerant of or vulnerable to these kinds of irrational claims.

Profiteers often exploit people's vulnerability to conspiracy theories and the fear they can induce. The National Rifle Association's most effective membership and fund-raising campaigns have long been accompanied by allegations of various politicians' "secret agendas" to confiscate guns. During the Obama years, outfits like "Tea Party Contacts" and "Food 4 Patriots" explained to their followers that FEMA* was hording MREs (meal-ready-to-eat) in preparation for an imminent food crisis. But "patriots" could get them from these vendors at low prices, or they could get a complete survival kit for just $39.

Conspiracy theories and political disinformation are propagated by AI (artificial intelligence) algorithms used by social media companies like Facebook and YouTube for maximizing their viewership and advertising revenue. The algorithms can be useful to subscribers or consumers by filtering out unwanted products and content, and by making recommendations that align with the users' interests. We have all seen how Amazon will recommend products that are similar to what we have previously purchased or viewed on that platform, for example.

The problem arises when the algorithms direct people to political propaganda and other kinds of articles at the exclusion of alternative views. Researchers at Google Deep Mind found that "feedback loops in recommendation systems can give rise to 'echo chambers' and 'filter bubbles,' which can narrow a user's content exposure and ultimately shift their worldview." As former YouTube engineer Guillame Chaslot explained in a tweet, "The YouTube algorithm I worked on heavily promoted Brexit, because divisiveness is efficient for watch time, and watch time leads to ads"—the ads from which the platform makes a great deal of money.

YouTube users spend 700 million hours per day watching videos recommended by YouTube's algorithm. Facebook's news feed algorithm drives some 950 million hours of viewing time each day. Research has found that salacious or divisive content drives

---

* Federal Emergency Management Agency

greater engagement among users, ensuring a greater distribution of the material. A recent study found that, during the campaigns ahead of the 2020 election, disinformation on Facebook got six times more clicks than factual news stories.[20] Even when a user flags deceptive or inappropriate content, their activity has already given a positive signal to the algorithm simply by having viewed it.[21]

Just as the repeal of the Fairness Doctrine resulted in greater political division and a proliferation of disinformation, social media companies' algorithms are further hardening extreme political views, and reinforcing erroneous claims and conspiracy theories.

Of course, misconception sometimes has little to do with political propaganda, alluring conspiracy theories, fraud schemes, or profiteering. It can simply be the result of an inadequate understanding of science or its application. The antivaccine movement, efforts to remove fluoride from public water supplies, and fears of cell phones, microwaves, or genetically engineered food crops are all examples.

There has been some level of resistance to vaccines as long as there have been vaccines. America's first and most famous scientist, Benjamin Franklin, was skeptical of the smallpox inoculation when he was young, writing an article criticizing it in 1721. In his 1791 autobiography, however, he expressed regret for that judgment.

> In 1736 I lost one of my sons, a fine boy of four years old, by the smallpox taken in the common way. I long regretted bitterly and still regret that I had not given it to him by inoculation. This I mention for the sake of the parents who omit that operation, on the supposition that they should never forgive themselves if a child died under it; my example showing that the regret may be the same either way, and that, therefore, the safer should be chosen.

By "if a child died under it," Franklin was referring to the risk of inoculation at that time, which incurred a two-percent chance of being fatal, while an infection without inoculation had about a fifteen-percent chance of being fatal. Once the cowpox vaccine was developed in 1798, the risks associated with inoculation dropped to nearly zero.[22]

So, there has long been some fear of vaccines. That fear was significantly heightened, however, in 1998 when British surgeon Andrew Wakefield submitted a scientific paper that was published in the prestigious British peer-reviewed medical journal, *The Lancet.* His paper claimed to have demonstrated that childhood vaccines for measles, mumps, and rubella (MMR) were linked to autism. The impact proved to be enormous, as Shawn Otto explained:

> The paper gave Wakefield instant celebrity because it crystallized the amorphous public fear of poison by science. Autism, after all, was inexplicably on the rise, and science had earned a reputation for this sort of thing: the spread of poisonous chemicals in the environment; the insertion of chemicals into foods; the destruction of the ozone layer; the obfuscation of links between smoking and cancer; and, in the early twentieth century, the injection of syphilis, cancer, and other diseases into patients (often children), federal prisoners, and African Americans—without their knowledge—so researchers could study the diseases.[23]

Wakefield did speaking-tours, coauthored a book, and became widely known. As it turned out, however, his conclusions were not just wrong, but fraudulent. He had fiddled with his evidence in order to make it fit a preconceived conclusion. *The Lancet* withdrew his paper and the British General Medical Council said Wakefield's "conduct in this regard was dishonest and irresponsible."[24]

Nevertheless, Wakefield's claims continued to circulate, and fearful parents have been confused about who to believe. Immunologists continue to be engaged in a battle to tamp down irrational fear and misconception.

Fear of the MMR vaccine was seen mostly among liberal, well-educated parents as a result of a misguided social trend stemming from misinformation. After controversy arose surrounding the advocacy of vaccinating adolescent girls against the sexually-transmitted papillomavirus (HPV), and when antigovernment libertarians' objections to government-mandated vaccines grew, resistance to vaccines began to appear on the political Right. Then, with the arrival of the COVID-19 pandemic in 2020 and an abundance of misinformation on Fox News and other conservative broadcast media and websites over the following year, a new group of anti-vaxxers arose—mostly less-educated, blue-collar consumers of right-wing media—even though President Trump had been vaccinated and had tacitly encouraged vaccination.

Despite COVID-19 having killed well over half a million Americans, a March 2021 NPR/PBS/Maris poll found that 49 percent of Republic men said they were choosing not to be vaccinated.[25] By July, after COVID-19 vaccines had become readily available, a Washington Post-ABC News poll found that only 45 percent of Republicans had been vaccinated, while 86 percent of Democrats had received the injections.[26] Along with Fox and other television outlets, numerous right-wing radio broadcasters also cast doubt on the efficacy of COVID vaccinations. By October of 2021, at least five of those broadcasters had died as a result of being infected with the virus.[27]

Fluoride is a mineral that occurs naturally in rocks, soil, and water. Because it was discovered to prevent tooth decay in the 1930s, fluoride is often added to toothpaste and public water supplies where it is not already present. Some water supplies have too much naturally-occurring fluoride, so it is reduced to achieve an optimum level. A great many studies from the 1930s until today have consistently demonstrated the safety and efficacy of fluoridated water.

Nevertheless, "anti-fluoridationists" have disputed those scientific studies in favor of internet lore about how fluoride "lowers IQ and causes everything from acne to anemia to Alzheimer's," among other ailments. The movement has become so powerful that cities have begun removing fluoride from public water supplies and the Texas Republican Party opposed water fluoridation in its 2018 platform. The disinformation and hysteria have risen to such a level that the Director of Public Health in Grand Rapids, Michigan, Dr. Winston Prothro has been "called a murderer and a communist" for telling the truth about fluoridated water.[28]

Building on the great successes of the selective breeding of food crops, genetically modified food crops or GMOs (genetically modified organisms) first appeared in the 1990s. Both methods change the genetic makeup of organisms. They just do it in different ways.

Traditional selective breeding uses naturally occurring gene mutations as plants with the desired traits are selected and others discarded. The process is imprecise and requires numerous generations to affect significant genetic changes. The traditional breeder can choose which plant parents to cross, but the results are unpredictable, given the random recombination of genes. Traditional methods limit the possible outcomes and lengthen the time needed to achieve significant results.

Genetic engineering, on the other hand, permits a highly targeted transfer of genes. The genes of new varieties can be easily analyzed, increasing the efficiency of developing new crop varieties with a wider range of desired traits—traits such as disease or insect resistance, herbicide tolerance, less delicate structure, and/or greater yields with less fertilizer.[29]

From a food safety standpoint, there is no significant difference. New plants created from traditional parent plants have the same nutritional content. And yet, a 2016 Pew Research

Center/AAAS* study found that only 37 percent of the general public believe genetically modified food crops are safe.

There are some legitimate concerns that can be raised about GMO products, like a more liberal use of pesticides and herbicides, the possible effects on pollinators, the corporate ownership of genomes, or restrictions on farmers' ability to harvest and reuse their own seeds, for example. But the plants themselves are as safe as other food crops.

Our complicated world will undoubtedly bring more disinformation through political propaganda, conspiracy theories, and simple misunderstandings of science. And malevolent actors like Russia, Iran, North Korea, and China will look for opportunities to exploit gullibility. Therefore, we should be vigilant in holding our elected officials accountable for telling the truth. When they engage in distorting, denying, or discrediting science, we all suffer. That often happens as a result of industry interests endeavoring to affect public policy, or the predisposed inclinations of individual politicians and their cultural ideologies. Since the Republican Party and the political Right have often been more closely aligned with energy business interests and social conservatism, that is where a denial of science has been most common in recent years. But we should be under no illusion that resistance to science is only found on the political Right.

In April of 1994, eight tobacco company CEOs testified before Congress, under oath, that they did not believe their tobacco products containing nicotine were addictive. By that time, science had, for many years, clearly shown that it was. The tobacco industry has spent enormous sums in political contributions and lobbying efforts to stem regulation, both at the state and federal government levels. Their support among politicians has never been partisan. It is regional. The politicians in whose states the industries reside have always been their staunchest defenders, regardless of political party. Most importantly, this is another vivid illustration of how the short-

---

* American Association for the Advancement of Science

term economic interests of a few people very often affects public policy at the expense of many.

Along with the political forces that endanger public health in the short-term are those that undermine the long-term prospects for humanity. On numerous occasions, American presidents have appointed cabinet members and staff who put short-term business interests and personal ideologies ahead of the public interest. For example, in his first term President Ronald Reagan appointed James G. Watt to be Secretary of the Department of the Interior, which oversees the Bureau of Indian Affairs, the Bureau of Land Management, the Bureau of Ocean Energy Management, the National Park Service, and the Environmental Protection Agency, among other entities. While Watt often proclaimed a commitment to conservation, he was described as an "anti-environmentalist," in part because of his enthusiastic promotion of the development of public lands, and his resistance to accepting the donations of private lands for the purpose of conservation. As Watt put it, "my responsibility is to follow the Scriptures, which call upon us to occupy the land until Jesus returns."[30] "We will mine more, drill more, cut more timber."[31] A joke reportedly circulated among corporate executives that asked: "How much power does it take to stop a million environmentalists? One Watt."[32]

President Reagan's successor, George H.W. Bush, on the other hand, was largely a champion of science and environmental protection. He told the U.N. Intergovernmental Panel on Climate Change that, "We know that the future of the Earth must not be compromised. We bear a sacred trust in our tenancy here and a covenant with those most precious to us—our children and theirs."

Apart from the skepticism of government that was espoused by Ronald Reagan, in those years many Republicans were fully engaged with environmental concerns. After all, it had been Republican President Richard Nixon who, in addition to creating the Environmental Protection Agency in 1970, helped to facilitate the

National Environmental Policy Act in 1969, an extension of the Clean Air Act in 1970, the Marine Mammal Protection Act in 1972, the Endangered Species Act in 1973, and the Safe Drinking Water Act in 1974.

In 1990, President Bush was instrumental in the passage of crucially needed amendments to the Clean Air Act. Upon Bush's death in 2018, Environmental Defense Fund president Fred Krupp described the effects of those changes.

> Thanks to President Bush, we don't hear much about acid rain these days. That is because the cap-and-trade system he championed has been phenomenally effective in cutting the sulfur dioxide that causes acid rain, reducing national average levels of the pollution by 88 percent since 1990.[33]

Rhea Suh, president of the Natural Resources Defense Council said in a statement,

> By cutting pollution from cars, trucks, power plants and other sources, the measures have sharply reduced toxic chemicals in the air we breathe, dangerous ozone, and the acid rain that was destroying American forests. The measures decreased asthma attacks, bronchitis, heart disease and other ills, preventing some 200,000 premature deaths and 20 million lost days at work or school every year to deliver up to $90 in public health benefits for every dollar invested in compliance.[34]

This example, along with other successes of the Clean Air Act and the Clear Water Act in dramatically improving air and water quality since the 1970s, is a testament to the effectiveness of public initiatives. And yet, simplistic ideologies and short-sighted business interests have continued to thwart good and practical governance.

The second President Bush held more of an ideological view of public policy—an ideology shaped in part by the business interests of those in his immediate orbit. George W. Bush selected Dick Cheney to be his vice president and close advisor. Cheney had a long history in politics and public service, but had most recently been CEO of Halliburton, a company steeped in the oil and gas industry. Bush himself had tried his hand at oil and gas exploration and knew many of the nation's top oil company executives personally.

In what many perceived to be a surrender to the oil, gas, and coal industries, in his first 100 days in office, Bush reneged on a campaign promise to cut CO_2 emissions from coal-burning power plants and announced that the United States would not implement the Kyoto climate change treaty. Christine Todd Whitman, who was his head of the EPA at that time, would later describe the exit from Kyoto as "the equivalent to 'flipping the bird,' frankly, to the rest of the world."[35]

In 2004, NASA scientist James Hansen publicly accused the Bush Administration of trying to suppress data showing an acceleration in the warming of the planet. In 2008, Jason Burnett, a former EPA official, wrote a letter to the Senate describing efforts by Vice President Cheney's office and the White House Council on Environmental Quality to block any discussion of the dangers of climate change. Burnett also said the White House had doctored scientific findings on the costs of fuel-efficiency standards in order to get around a 2007 Supreme Court ruling that compelled the EPA to regulate auto emissions.[36]

The Bush Administration also targeted the Endangered Species Act, particularly with concerns that its protection of polar bears could limit oil drilling in the Arctic. An Inspector General report found that Julie McDonald, who was Deputy Secretary of the Interior Department and headed the endangered species program at the U.S. Fish and Wildlife Service, had repeatedly blocked new species from being added to the endangered species list. Upon her 2007 resignation, biologist and head of the service, Dale Hall, described McDonald's tenure as "a blemish on the scientific integrity of the Fish and Wildlife Service and the Department of the Interior."[37]

The Bush Administration opened millions of acres of wilderness to oil and gas drilling, mining, and logging; defunded toxic waste cleanup programs; endorsed commercial whaling operations; approved mountain-top removal for coal mining; weakened EPA enforcement; and, despite the work of his father, "gutted key sections of the Clean Water and Clean Air Acts."[38]

In his last days in office, Bush undertook a burst of additional deregulations for the benefit of oil and gas and logging interests. But he also did something that was unexpected. With only two weeks left in office, Bush created national monuments protecting nearly 200,000 square miles in the Pacific Ocean. This prompted Joshua Reichert, Managing Director of the Pew Environmental Group, to say, "We and others in the environmental community have been at odds with this administration on lots of things, but if one looks at this one event it is a significant conservation event."[39]

After he left office, President Bush's activities have demonstrated that he is an extraordinarily decent man. His extensive charitable endeavors have included supporting HIV prevention and treatment in Africa, civil rights, disaster relief, cancer research, human rights campaigns, and numerous other worthy causes. Furthermore, he demonstrated there are limits to his partisanship when he said that right-wing domestic terrorists possess the "same foul spirit" as Islamic terrorists. Nevertheless, the ill-advised and costly Iraq War and his environmental record will undoubtedly mar his legacy forever. It is not just the immediate damage that was incurred in the 2000s, it was his use of government to undermine public confidence in science that has lived on.

Indeed, it is the undermining of the scientific institutions of the United States government, as well as those of the world, that should be of great concern to us. In the United States, we saw their biggest challenges under the administration of Donald Trump. It was a time when scientific integrity and honest analysis were forced to take a back seat to the president's ego and his extraordinarily limited understanding of science and the world.

In addition to his landmark changes to the Clean Air Act in 1990, President George H.W. Bush had established the U.S. Global Research Program that uses 13 federal agencies to monitor changes to our planet's ecosystems. As part of the program, the legislation mandated a National Climate Assessment be published every four years. (The first concluded in 2000.) When the Fourth National Climate Assessment was completed in 2018, it explained how climate change would cost tens of billions of dollars in economic impact, as well as the lives of more Americans each year. President Trump simply said he didn't believe it.

It is well known that President Trump doesn't read, beyond short documents. (His staff reported that they regularly included pictures in documents they presented to him in order to hold his attention.) Trump himself explained that his understanding of the world was shaped by watching "the shows" on television—primarily Fox News, where denials of science are regular fare.[40] At least two studies have shown that Fox News has long dealt with the subject of climate change, as well as other scientific knowledge, in an ideological context, rather than objectively reporting fact-based science.[41] Fox presents deniers of human-induced climate change in more prominent argumentative positions, despite their being less than 3 percent of scientists. As a result, Trump doesn't believe in the science of climate change, and is rather skeptical of most science.

Science Magazine wrote that Trump's "repeated public denials of scientific expertise and his disdain for evidence have prompted many researchers to label him the most anti-science president in living memory."[42] Most alarming was his willingness and ability to induce government scientists or political appointees to alter documents for the sake of his ego or his personal political ambition. Perhaps most absurd was his alteration of a National Weather Service forecast map, not because he disagreed with the prediction, but because of an inability to admit even a simple, largely harmless error.

In September of 2019, Trump tweeted that Hurricane Dorian was headed toward the states of Florida, Georgia, and Alabama. The National Weather Service in Birmingham, Alabama quickly corrected the error to allay fears by tweeting, "Alabama will NOT see any impacts from #Dorian." Three days later, Trump provided an update in the Oval Office and displayed a forecast map that had been crudely altered with a Sharpie to include Alabama. Pressure from the White House then prompted a new statement, crafted by political appointees at the Commerce Department, to be released from NOAA* backing Trump's claim and disparaging the career scientists at the National Weather Service in Birmingham for telling the truth.[43]

In his annual budget requests, President Trump consistently proposed deep cuts to most of the agencies that do science. Fortunately, Congress ignored many of those recommendations. In fact, funding for the National Institutes of Health, the largest federal facilitator of academic research, rose by 39 percent over a five-year period that included Trump's tenure, and funding for the National Science Foundation rose by 17 percent over the last three years of his administration. Trump did propose increases in research for artificial intelligence and quantum information, doubling the funding for those programs over two years.[44]

But when Congress would not go along with Trump Administration proposals for deep cuts to two USDA** research agencies, he found another way to undermine them. The USDA had published objective research findings regarding the impacts of climate change, the efficiency of food assistance programs, and the impact of Trump tax cuts on small farms versus wealthy agribusinesses. Trump didn't like the conclusions, so he sought to punish the agencies.

The National Institute of Food and Agriculture and the Economic Research Service were moved out of Washington D.C. to

---

* The National Oceanic and Atmospheric Administration, under which the National Weather Service is structured. NOAA is a bureau of the Commerce Department.
** United States Department of Agriculture

Kansas City, Missouri. The director of government relations for the American Economic Association, Katherine Smith Evans, who ran the Economic Research Service under both George W. Bush and Barack Obama, described the effect. "The agencies have been decimated. Their ability to perform the functions they were created to perform—it doesn't exist anymore."

As predicted, half of the agencies' most experienced researchers, working at the top of their fields, resigned, rather than uproot their families and move. ERS economist Laura Dodson said, "We've lost hundreds, if not thousands, of staff-years of expertise."[45]

The Trump Administration repeatedly sidelined or over-ruled expert scientists to further political objectives. At the EPA, administrator Scott Pruitt removed the agency's web page on climate change, "fired and barred independent scientific advisors who had received grants from the EPA (a policy that a court ultimately found to be illegal) and then replaced them with industrial representatives." William K. Reilly, who had been EPA administrator under the first President Bush, would later remark, "There's no precedent for the attack on science, the sweep of it, the blatancy of it that we saw in the [Trump] administration."[46]

Only halfway through the Trump term, a bipartisan report from New York University, led by former U.S. Attorney Preet Bharara and former EPA head Christine Todd Whitman, found that science in federal agencies was being pushed to a "crisis." As Lisa Friedman at the New York Times wrote,

> In a single month in 2017, the Trump administration's Environmental Protection Agency blocked scientists from speaking at a climate change conference, its Interior Department forwarded a policy letter to U.S. Customs and Border Protection only after deleting concerns from biologists about a border wall's effects on wildlife, and the F.B.I. issued a crime report that omitted dozens of tables of data on homicides and arrests. That October was fairly typical for the Trump administration.

The report noted some of the offenses of other administrations, such as those of the George W. Bush Administration described above, and the Obama Administration's last-minute changes to an EPA report to downplay the risks of oil and gas fracking to public water supplies. But it expressed the most alarm at what the Trump Administration was doing. In an email, Ms. Whitman wrote, "While the threat to the independence of scientific data did not start with the administration, it has certainly accelerated of late."[47]

Mr. Bharara said in an interview, "There's truth and there's science, and that shouldn't be swayed by whether someone is a liberal or a conservative, a Democrat or a Republican." Nevertheless, when legislation was proposed by U.S. Representative Paul Tonko to develop "scientific integrity standards" to discourage political interference in scientific research and reporting, the legislation garnered 217 co-sponsors, but none were Republican.[48]

In the final year of the Trump Administration, the COVID-19 pandemic resulted in new assaults on the integrity of science and federal agencies. Congressional investigators uncovered emails from Trump appointees who touted their ability to block or alter scientific reports so they would align with Trump's optimistic public comments about the pandemic.[49] Trump staffers, Republican members of Congress, and talking heads on Fox News endeavored to undermine the work and the credibility of Dr. Anthony Fauci, who had been an advisor on infectious diseases to every president since Ronald Reagan, because his assessment of the pandemic and his recommendations for its mitigation did not fit with those of the president.

Trump worried that shutdowns would unduly affect the economy and, thereby, hinder his chances of reelection. So, as he admitted to Bob Woodward in an interview for Woodward's book, *Rage*, he had intentionally "downplayed" the lethality of the virus.[50]

Dr. Deborah Birx, who headed President Trump's coronavirus task force, later said that Trump's downplaying the pandemic may have cost the lives of hundreds of thousands of Americans.[51] (To be fair, it should be noted that President Trump's "Operation Warp Speed" very likely expedited the process of vaccine development, and the vaccines have saved the lives of hundreds of thousands of people.)

In September 2020, the U.S. National Academy of Sciences and the National Academy of Medicine issued a joint statement in response to reports of political interference in the work of government scientists. It was an unusual rebuke from these highly respected private institutions.

> Policymaking must be informed by the best available evidence without it being distorted, concealed, or otherwise deliberately miscommunicated. We find ongoing reports and incidents of the politicization of science, particularly the overriding of evidence and advice from public health officials and derision of government scientists, to be alarming. ... Any efforts to discredit the best science and scientists threaten the health and welfare of us all.[52]

Indeed, the health and welfare of us all will depend on our own understanding of what is at stake and our ability to discern what is real and what is not—what is the truth and what is propaganda.

Some readers may be thinking this chapter has been too political, partisan, or polemic for a book about objective science. Yet, a book about how humankind has altered the planet must include a discussion of human nature and the resulting political forces that resist responsible mitigation of the environmental hazards of our own making.

A recent Washington Post-ABC News poll found that, from 2014 to 2021, the percentage of self-identified Democrats who see climate change as a serious problem rose from 84 percent to 95 percent, while the percentage of Republicans who see climate change as a serious problem fell from 49 percent to 39 percent over the same period. The findings corresponded with annual polling by the Gallup organization.

It behooves us, therefore, to understand how this disparity has occurred. We need to know how misinformation is propagated. We need to know how misconception and tribal thinking occur and how they affect political forces and, ultimately, public policy.

The United States certainly cannot solve the problem of climate change alone. It will require the cooperation of the world, and enlisting the cooperation of authoritarian governments is the biggest challenge. But we cannot expect others to comply if we fail to refute disinformation, except reality, and lead the world.

The founding fathers of the United States believed in science. Benjamin Franklin was an experimenter and an inventor, creating such things as the lightning rod, bifocal glasses, and swim fins. Franklin founded the American Philosophical Society which would become the preeminent association of scientists in America for many decades. Thomas Jefferson served as president of the Society for two of those decades, including during his tenure as president of the United States.

Jefferson collected scientific instruments and fossils, including the fossilized bones of an extinct North American ground sloth species that would come to be named after him—*Megalonyx jeffersonii*. In addition to several other geographic expeditions, Jefferson famously supported the Lewis and Clark expedition that facilitated subsequent westward exploration and settlement.

The founders also believed that a well-informed electorate is essential for the success of democracy. As James Madison wrote, "A diffusion of knowledge is the only guardian of true liberty." Ever the purveyor of insight and clever prose, Benjamin Franklin explained, "On education all our lives depend; And few to that, too few, with care attend." In addition to the preservation of liberty, a diffusion of knowledge and caring is essential to the preservation of our home, planet Earth.

We do not all need to be fully versed in the scientific knowledge of the world. But we do need to understand the value of critical thinking, and to refrain from the laziness of blind adherences to dogmas or ideologies, or indiscriminate belief in the claims of politicians and cable news personalities. We should be well aware that one of the definitions of "politics" is the "use of intrigue or strategy in obtaining any position of power or control," and a synonym for "intrigue" is "chicanery"—trickery. We should also be aware that more than a few newspapers, most cable news outlets, and all politicians engage in politics.

This doesn't mean we cannot trust anything politicians say. We simply need to be aware their agenda is almost always self-promotion to stay in power before and above all else. Often their self-promotion aligns with the wider public interest. But just as often, it will align with the interests of a particular faction and reelection campaign donors at the expense of the rest of society, and deception will be used to conceal the disparity.

So, it serves us well to be skeptical and to know enough about the world to know when politicians and television partisans are being deceptive—know enough to recognize that Texas Governor Greg Abbott was not being truthful about the causes of the power outages that February in 2021, and to recognize why.

8

Rays of Hope

A s a young man in the spring of 1974, I drove from Texas to Los Angeles, California for the first time. I travelled by way of Interstate 10, mostly under the clear skies of the desert Southwest. As I approached the pass between the San Bernardino and the San Jacinto Mountains, I saw what looked like the dark sky of a heavy rain ahead on the distant horizon. As I passed between the mountains, however, I came to realize that it was not rain I had seen. It was a thick, brownish-gray smog hovering over the Los Angeles Basin. It was air pollution.

Because of its unique geological character, the Los Angeles Basin continues to experience episodes of dangerous smog occasionally, but not anything like what I saw on that day in 1974, and not like a great many of the worst days going as far back as the 1940s. The air quality over Los Angeles has improved dramatically. This has been the result of both state and federal laws enacted to curb air pollution by regulating industrial and automobile exhaust emissions.

Federal legislation was passed in 1955, 1963, and 1967 to study the problem, but there was not much in those laws that could do anything about it. In 1970, President Richard Nixon created the Environmental Protection Agency (EPA) to enforce the newly enacted Clean Air Act. The new legislation authorized the creation of both federal and state regulations for limiting polluting emissions.

But it was not until 1975 that significant progress was made. By EPA mandate, that was the year all cars manufactured in the United States were to be fitted with catalytic converters—the "key piece of technology that allowed everything to change," according to California Air Resources Board chair Mary Nichols.[1] The result has been significant improvements in air quality over Los Angeles, as well as the rest of the nation.

To strengthen its effectiveness and to broaden its scope, the Clean Air Act was amended in 1977 and in 1990. Promoted by President H.W. Bush, the changes made in 1990 targeted the problem of acid rain. As we saw in the last chapter, the new law enjoyed great success in reducing the sulfur dioxide emissions that cause acid rain, improving the health of American forests, surface water, and people.

According to the EPA, the regulation of industrial and auto emissions has measurably improved the air we breathe. "Between 1990 and 2017, national concentrations of air pollutants improved 80 percent for lead, 77 percent for carbon monoxide, 88 percent for sulfur dioxide, 56 percent for nitrogen oxide, and 22 percent for ozone." In a peer-reviewed study, the EPA has found that hundreds of thousands of premature deaths and millions of respiratory illnesses have been averted as a result of the Clean Air Act.[2]

The 1972 Clean Water Act similarly sought to improve the water quality of America's lakes, streams, and rivers. Before its enactment, some rivers were so polluted with raw sewage and flammable toxins they could catch fire. In fact, a fire on the Cuyahoga River in Cleveland, Ohio in 1969 provided the needed impetus for passage of the legislation.[3]

Researchers at the University of California Berkley and Iowa State University found that, after enactment of the Clean Water Act, "Most of 25 water pollution measures showed improvement, including an increase in dissolved oxygen concentrations and a decrease in fecal coliform bacteria. The share of rivers safe for fishing increased by 12 percent between 1972 and 2001."[4]

Critics will point to studies that have concluded that, unlike the Clean Air Act, where the economic benefits have clearly been shown to outweigh the economic costs of the act, the Clean Water Act appears to cost more than its economic benefits.[5] Such studies, however, have mostly considered property values with too little emphasis on public health, recreation values, and the effects on wildlife, all of which are more difficult to quantify. As noted by Joseph Shapiro, co-author of one economic study, "drinking water treatment plants test for a few hundred different chemicals and U.S. industry produces, processes, or imports closer to 33,000, and so it is possible there are chemicals that existing studies don't measure that have important consequences for well-being." For fairly obvious reasons, Gallup polls have consistently shown the top environmental concern of most Americans is water pollution, above air pollution and climate change.[6] The great value of clean water to human health and wellbeing is well understood around the world.

Forty-five years ago, the majestic symbol of America, the American bald eagle, was on the verge of extinction throughout most of its range. Habitat destruction, illegal shooting, and the poisoning of its food sources due to the widespread use of the pesticide DDT had nearly wiped out the bald eagle, along with the golden eagle, the American peregrine falcon, and the California condor.[7]

The bald eagle first came under federal protection in 1940, with the Bald Eagle Protection Act. The act was soon amended to include the golden eagle. Then, the 1966 Endangered Species Preservation Act authorized the acquisition of land to preserve "selected species of native fish and wildlife." The 1969 Endangered Species Conservation Act expanded on the 1966 act by authorizing the compilation of a list of animals that were "threatened with worldwide extinction" and prohibited their import without a permit. Included were birds, mammals, amphibians, fish, crustaceans, and mollusks.[8]

In 1972, eagles fell under the Migratory Bird Treaty Act when the United States and Mexico agreed to amend a 1936 migratory bird convention. Signatories of the 1936 treaty were the United States, Mexico, Canada, Japan, and Russia.

Little progress was made, however, until the EPA banned DDT in 1972 and President Richard Nixon and the United States Congress created the Endangered Species Act (ESA) in 1973. The new law required the protection of critical habitats and mandated recovery plans for listed species. The law required a coordination of strategies among federal, state, tribal, and local efforts to prevent extinctions. Currently, the Act protects more than 1,600 plant and animal species in the United States and its territories.[9] Once a species is no longer in peril, it is removed from the list.

The Endangered Species Act has been a remarkable success. About 99 percent of species that have fallen under its protection have avoided extinction. Scientists estimate hundreds of species would have been lost, but for the ESA. And more than 110 have significantly recovered—species like the Aleutian Canada goose, the black-footed ferret, the American crocodile, the short-nose sturgeon, the gray wolf, the whooping crane, the California condor, the peregrine falcon, and the bald eagle. As a result of the DDT ban and the Endangered Species Act, the American bald eagle has largely recovered and was removed from the Threatened and Endangered Species list on August 9, 2007.

The Endangered Species Act also supports international efforts in the preservation of species and prohibits the importation of threatened species into the United States. The ESA has frequently served as a model for other nations in creating their own conservation legislation.

In the 1970s, scientists discovered that human-emitted chlorofluorocarbons (CFCs) were dissolving Earth's protective ozone layer. Ozone, consisting of three oxygen atoms bonded together (O_3), is toxic to humans. But the layer of ozone in the upper atmosphere, a little more than 30 miles up, is essential in filtering out much of the sun's ultraviolet (UV) radiation that can cause skin cancer and cataracts. Excessive UV radiation can also harm marine ecosystems and plants, reducing the productivity of crops like soybeans, rice, and wheat.

Mostly in developed countries beginning in the 1960s, CFCs became widely used as safe and effective refrigerants in refrigerators, automobiles, and air conditioners. Their use was at a peak in the 1980s when a hole in the ozone layer over Antarctica was detected. Something had to be done—fast—and this time it would require the cooperation of the entire world.

In 1987, the Montreal Protocol on Substances that Deplete the Ozone Layer was adopted as a framework for international cooperation regarding the control of CFCs and halons on the basis of the Vienna Convention for the Protection of the Ozone Layer. The United States ratified the treaty in 1988 and has joined four subsequent amendments. The Montreal Protocol is the first treaty in history to be ratified by every country in the world. As President Ronald Reagan proclaimed,

> The Montreal Protocol is a model of cooperation. It is a product of the recognition and international consensus that ozone depletion is a global problem, both in terms of its causes and its effects. The protocol is the result of an extraordinary process of scientific study, negotiations among representatives of the business and environmental communities, and international diplomacy. It is a monumental achievement.[10]

The EPA has estimated that, as a result of the treaty, Americans are "expected to avoid 443 million cases of skin cancer, approximately 2.3 million skin-cancer deaths, and more than 63 million cases of cataracts, with even greater benefits worldwide." By the middle of the 21st century, the ozone layer is expected to approach a full recovery of its density before the use of CFCs.[11]

The successes of the Clean Air Act, the Clean Water Act, the Endangered Species Act, and the Montreal Protocol tell us that legislation works, and effective international agreements are possible. These successes along with international agreements of the 1992 U.N. Framework Convention on Climate Change, the 1997 Kyoto Protocol, and the 2016 Paris Climate Accord tell us there is room for hope that humanity can rise to the environmental challenges facing our world. We need only to make sure it does.

There are a number of things we can do. Firstly, we can work to elect leaders who understand the issues and have the courage and the leadership skills to effectively enact needed legislation. Such elected officials will have to lead the skeptics of our nation and the world to a better understanding of what is at stake and what can be done. An American president, for example, must be able to muster enough international influence and power to ensure all nations keep their commitments, much like we saw with the Montreal Protocol.

Secondly, we can behave responsibly as individuals, as consumers, and as corporate leaders. We can support cultural trends and practices that encourage greater responsibility among all the world's people. Cultural trends are powerful forces in affecting political trends and societal change. We can commit ourselves to conservation and sustainable consumption, and encourage others to do the same. We can choose to do business only with those small companies and large corporations that behave responsibly.

Some of the world's largest and most powerful corporations are already adapting, despite the political forces that lag behind— primarily as a result of anticipated consumer demand. General Motors (GM), for example, has committed to making only electric cars and light-duty trucks by 2035.

It seems unlikely that GM's move toward electric cars is driven solely by concern for the planet. After all, GM's chief executive, Mary T. Barra, had told President Trump that Obama-era fuel efficiency standards were too hard on manufacturers, prompting Trump to significantly relax the standards, adding nearly a billion more tons of carbon dioxide to the atmosphere. Instead, the move is driven mostly by anticipated consumer demand and anticipated government mandates. After all, the growth of Tesla's market share has begun to accelerate. Furthermore, China has mandated that most new cars sold there by 2035 will be electric and, through its joint ventures, GM sells more cars in China than it does in the U.S.[12]

Great Britain, Ireland, and the Netherlands have also announced they will ban the sale of new gasoline and diesel engine vehicles beginning in 2030.[13] As a result of upcoming government mandates and consumer trends, a host of other car companies are moving toward hybrid and electric cars and light trucks. Here are some of their promises:

- Ford—carbon neutral by 2050
- Mazda, Mitsubishi, and Nissan—net-zero carbon emissions by 2050
- Honda—all electric or hydrogen fuel-cell by 2040
- Volkswagen—electric in Europe by 2035 (but not other markets)
- GM—all electric by 2035
- Audi—all electric by 2033
- Subaru—40 percent hybrid or electric by 2030
- Kia—40 percent electric by 2030
- Volvo—all electric by 2030
- Jaguar—all electric by 2025

Given the nature of competition, there is a good chance some of these automakers will strive to go electric faster than their current projections.

Commercial vehicles are going electric too. Tesla is making an electric long-haul big rig, prompting Walmart, PepsiCo, and UPS to commit to buying them. UPS expects an initial delivery of 125 heavy-duty Class 8 electric semi-trucks by next year. More will follow.

UPS, Amazon, and FedEx delivery vehicles are all going electric because it has become a more efficient and cost-effective option. The cost of batteries for vehicles has plummeted in recent years and continues to fall, due to new technologies and enormous investments in production capacity, largely in China.[14] (While too many American politicians balk at supporting green technologies, China is looking forward to leading the world.)

UPS is working with suppliers to redesign its trucks, while investing in the infrastructure for charging stations. UPS Senior Director of Maintenance and Engineering Scott Phillippi expects the new trucks will cost 20 percent less to operate than traditional diesel vehicles and, with their "tremendous torque," will be more efficient in their stop and go deliveries.[15]

Naturally, as automobiles and trucks move toward zero emissions, the energy companies that produce gasoline and diesel will be forced to adapt. But it won't be without a struggle.

In September of 2019, Politico reported that groups backed by oil industry giants like ExxonMobil and the Koch brothers' empire are waging a state-by-state, multimillion-dollar battle against electric cars and their needed infrastructure. Trade groups like the American Petroleum Institute, the Western States Petroleum Association, the American Fuel and Petrochemical Manufacturers, and lobbying organizations like the Koch brothers-funded Americans for Prosperity have opposed tax credits for electric vehicles, supported the Trump Administration's roll-back of Obama-era fuel efficiency standards, opposed utility companies' installation of charging stations at places like grocery stores and rest stops, and opposed Colorado's new zero-emission vehicle mandate. Most of these efforts, however, have simply delayed progress, rather than stopping it.[16] Ultimately, consumer demand will rule the trend toward electric or hydrogen fuel-cell vehicles.

Most of the world's major oil companies have now set net-zero emission targets for the year 2050. These goals refer to the gases—mostly carbon dioxide and methane—emitted in the processes of extracting, transporting, and refining oil and natural gas, not the companies' products of oil and natural gas themselves. Nevertheless, that is a lot of carbon. A 2018 Stanford University study found that "in 2015, nearly 9,000 oilfields in 90 countries produced greenhouse gases equivalent to 1.7 gigatons of carbon dioxide—roughly 5 percent of all emissions from fuel combustion that year."[17] If oil companies can arrest these emissions, it would be a significant leap forward. Their incentive to do so will be driven by consumers and, in part, the world's banks.

In 2019, "some 130 banks (about one-third of the world's banks) with combined assets of $47 trillion committed to aligning their businesses to the Paris Climate Agreement." The banks, particularly those in Europe, are increasingly sensitive to public pressure to refrain from funding fossil fuels. Some have already said they would no longer provide project-specific financing for coal-fired power plants, Arctic oil exploration, or oil sands extraction. Morgan Stanley, a major lender for fossil fuel projects, was "the first U.S. bank to start measuring the emissions generated by the businesses it lends to and invests in."[18] This is an example of how the business philosophies of some corporations are changing.

The decade of the 1980s is sometimes called the decade of greed. After having begun during the Jimmy Carter presidency, the deregulation of industries was accelerated during the presidency of Ronald Reagan. It was a time when the economic philosophy of Milton Friedman took hold—a time when much of the business culture would declare, "greed is good."[19] In his 1962 book, *Capitalism and Freedom*, Friedman had argued that, "There is one and only one social responsibility of business...to increase its profits." Ever since, that emphasis on short-term profits above all else has resulted in a perception of an adversarial relationship between big business and the interests of the public at large.[20]

Further tainting the image of "giant corporations" (a phrase used as a pejorative by some politicians on the Left) has been the unscrupulous behavior of some, such as those that have hidden toxic dumping or destructive practices while lobbying for less account-ability. The tobacco industry, for example, was able to deny the harmful effects of smoking and gain protection from politicians for many years. The effectiveness with which some companies and industries are able to get favored treatment from public officials furthers the image of conscienceless behemoths with unwarranted power. More recently, however, more and more companies are coming to recognize the value of good citizenship.

Because it is increasingly good for their public relations— good for business—a lot of companies, big and small, are going green. As Allstate Corporation chief executive Tom Wilson explained in a 2016 op-ed, "We must reject narrow definitions of what a corporation can and should do—and get on with making the world a better place."[21] Some companies have even designed their business plans around efforts to do what is right for the world.

ESG (Environmental, Social, Governance) ratings are now available to investors who prefer to invest in responsible companies. These ratings tell investors how companies compare to competitors in matters environmental impact, employee relations, and financially relevant corporate governance.

As more and more people now seek to buy from or invest in more responsible businesses, some companies engage in "corporate greenwashing," a practice of trying to look environmentally friendly without any meaningful effort. But, with a little research, it is possible to find environmentally responsible companies with which to do business. Here are a few examples:

tentree is a Canadian apparel company created with the intent of making sustainable products with environmentally responsible manufacturing. The company name is derived from its commitment to plant ten trees for each item sold. So far, they have planted more than 58 million trees in 10 countries and are striving for a billion trees by 2030. The company even offers a program they call "Climate+," where you can purchase extra trees to "offset your daily pleasures like extra-steamy showers, avocado toast and weekend getaways." The company uses natural fibers like cotton, hemp, and lyocell, and it minimizes the use of water and toxic chemicals in its manufacturing. With its offsets, tentree is "Climate Neutral Certified."

Climate Neutral is a separate nonprofit organization that helps companies measure, offset, and reduce their carbon emissions, and it certifies those that are demonstrably carbon neutral. Once a brand meets the standard, its products can carry the "Climate Neutral Certified" label.

Patagonia is an American apparel company that tops most lists of environmentally responsible businesses. Its products are made of carefully sourced materials, often recycled fabrics such as nylon and polyester. It uses manufacturing processes that minimize waste and the use of toxic chemicals. Patagonia offers its customers a repair and reuse program called "Worn Wear" to reduce waste. The company has pledged to make its entire supply chain carbon-neutral by 2025.

Outerknown is an American apparel company co-founded by designer John Moore and 11-time world-champion surfer Kelly Slater. The company was created as part of Slater's long-time advocacy of a sustainable lifestyle. Ninety-percent of the fibers the company uses are "organic, recycled, or regenerated." All swim trunks are made of 100 percent "recycled or renewable fibers because there's nothing more epic than a clean ocean." Most admirable is a program to recycle used fishing nets into new nylon products, thereby reducing at least a portion of the world's estimated 640,000 tons of abandoned fishing nets that harm sea life.

Young Henrys Brewing is an Australian craft brewing company that uses microalgae to convert the CO_2 produced in the fermenting process of its beers into oxygen. The company estimates that, for each batch of brew, "their algae releases as much oxygen as two hectares of bushland."[22] The company also donates all of its spent grain to local farms for cattle feed. Solar panels on its roof provide the brewery with about 25 percent of its energy needs. More panels are coming.

Ecosia is a German search engine corporation that donates 80 percent of its profits to nonprofits specializing in reforestation. The company's efforts have planted more than 130 million trees (to date) in 9,000 locations around the world. Ecosia also supports small farms, wildlife protection, and biodiversity restoration. The company has built its own solar energy facility and its operations are powered exclusively by renewable energy. Ecosia is a "Certified B Corporation."

According to the nonprofit **B Lab** that evaluates companies and administers the certifications, "Certified B Corporations are businesses that meet the highest standards of verified social and environmental performance, public transparency, and legal accountability to balance profit and purpose."[23]

Seventh Generation is an American company owned by Unilever that distributes innovative eco-friendly cleaning, personal care, and paper products. The products are made of plant-based ingredients, with no synthetic dyes or fragrances, and are packaged in plant-based or recycled material containers. Seventh Generation is a Certified B Corporation.

Ikea, the world's largest furniture retailer, has invested in green energy, reforestation, and forest protection projects. The Swedish company has phased out all single-use plastic and uses only LED lighting in its stores. Its edible products are sourced from suppliers that follow sustainable farming practices.

Google is an American search engine company that has been carbon neutral for over a decade through its use of renewable energy sources and carbon offset schemes. "Google has cultivated its own bee colonies, grown food for office premises, and saved over 1 million pounds of imperfect produce from waste."[24]

New City Microcreamery in Hudson, Massachusetts and **Cajou Creamery** in Baltimore, Maryland, are two among a growing number of craft-style microcreameries offering dairy-free ice cream, eliminating the need for methane-producing cows. These establishments are responding to increasing demand by millennials and Generation Z consumers for animal-free products that replicate the texture and taste of dairy-based ice cream by using plant-based ingredients. Ice cream as well as confections are made with coconut milk and, in some cases, an innovative process using liquid nitrogen as a bonding agent to reduce sugar content.

In the case of New City Creamery, the application of the liquid nitrogen creates the spectacle of white fog enveloping the entire kitchen floor, which can be seen through plexiglass to the delight of children. "Global Market Insights, a consumer research firm, predicts that dairy-free ice cream will become a $1 billion industry worldwide by 2024."[25]

There are many other examples of retail establishments and other enterprises either working to improve the world or to minimize any negative impact of their operations. We do well to support these businesses.

Given the need to feed the coming world population of about 11 billion people, a few entrepreneurial companies (sometimes with a little nudge from governments) are developing new technologies to meet that challenge while minimizing further damage to our planet. The objectives are to increase available food supplies without further deforestation for agricultural tracts, to reduce agricultural greenhouse gas emissions, to increase fish stocks, and to restore natural ecosystems.

About one-third of food is wasted before it gets to con- sumers, mostly from spoilage. Several companies are working to develop natural compounds with which produce can be treated to slow ripening. A company called **Apeel Sciences**, for example, has developed a variety of thin, edible spray-on films that inhibit the growth of bacteria and preserve the moisture in fruits. **Nanology** and **Blueapple** are two more companies that have developed ways of inhibiting the spoilage of produce.[26]

As we saw in Chapter 3, crop breeding and genetic engineering have already improved food crop yields, reduced the need for polluting fertilizers, and reduced water consumption. Research continues to yield improvements in those areas and more. Low-methane rice, for example, is being developed to reduce methane emissions from rice paddies—currently about 15 percent of agricultural greenhouse gas emissions.

As wild fish stocks have been depleted, fish farming, or "aquaculture," has grown to meet consumer demand for fish. New aquaculture feeds using algae and oilseeds containing omega-3 fatty acids are being developed to reduce the need for harvesting smaller wild fish for ingredients in feeds for the larger farm fish. This helps to preserve small fish populations and wild ecosystems.[27]

While large-scale aquaculture operations can sometimes be destructive to the environment, a growing number of small-scale, family-owned fishing enterprises are turning to farming sea scallops and other bivalves in environmentally beneficial ways. The presence of farmed scallops, mussels, or oysters in local habitats filters the water, reinforces wild shellfish populations, and improves conditions for biodiversity, all the while providing a source of protein without the need for arable land, fresh water, or fertilizers.[28]

Similarly, kelp farming is a growing industry that does not deplete the oceans' resources. Instead, it improves ocean health. Susie Arnold, a marine scientist at the Island Institute in Rockland, Maine, explained, "Kelp is the superhero of seaweed. It de-acidifies the ocean by removing carbon dioxide, which we have too much of."

Kelp also absorbs nitrogen. As we saw in Chapter 4, fertilizers containing nitrogen regularly enter ocean ecosystems from runoff and create algae blooms that deplete oxygen and kill sea life. Kelp farmed at specific points of fertilizer runoff and wastewater treatment discharges can help to mitigate the effects of excessive nitrogen entering ocean waters. Kelp at these locations can then be harvested and used as a more natural fertilizer.[29]

Kelp is not only beneficial to the sea, chefs are discovering varieties that are very nutritious and quite tasty, adding them to their menus. Kelp is relatively easy to grow, and has an abundance of iron, potassium, calcium, iodine, fiber and vitamins.

Harvesting wild kelp is an ancient practice, but farming kelp is relatively new. It is proving to be another sustainable food source without the need for fresh water, fertilizers, or chemicals.[30] As we will see below, kelp also appears to significantly reduce methane emissions from cows when added to their feed.

At least a third of agricultural greenhouse gas emissions come from cows—methane from farts and manure, but mostly from belching due to enteric fermentation. (Enteric fermentation is the digestive process of ruminant animals in which carbohydrates are broken down in the stomach by microorganisms into simple molecules for absorption into the blood stream. The by-product is methane that is belched out.) New technologies are being developed to capture and make use of the methane emitted from both ends of cows.

Biodigesters are tanks containing manure and/or food waste that are digested by anaerobic (living in the absence of oxygen) bacteria. The microorganic digestive process produces very small amounts of water vapor, carbon dioxide, methane, and a few other gases—but mostly methane, which can be captured and used as a combustible fuel. Biodigesters have been around for a long time. The first large scale plant was built at a leper colony in Bombay, India in 1859. Small biodigesters have been in use on farms, particularly dairy farms, for many years to reduce the volume of manure waste disposal. Some have been able to capture the methane to use as fuel, but most have failed to be economically viable. New practices and technologies, however, are making the process more productive.

Adding food waste, for example, adds income for small operators through fees paid by manufacturers, retailers, and others needing to dispose of the waste.[31] More importantly, more efficient systems are enabling the capture of enough methane to fuel the production of more electricity. Larger farms can even sell the methane or the electricity. Even larger operators that serve numerous farms are converting methane into natural gas for sale on the open market.

But manure accounts for only a small part of the methane cows emit. The harder task is to capture the methane of flatulence and belching—mostly the belching, which accounts for about 95 percent of a cow's methane emission. For that, new technologies are being imagined and tested.

Several companies are developing feed additives intended to reduce methane emissions. The Dutch company **DSM**, for example, has a product called 3-NOP that has reduced methane emissions by 30 percent in testing, with no apparent deleterious side effects.[32]

Research from the University of California at Davis, however, indicates that adding small amounts of seaweed to ruminant feeds can yield even better results—significantly better. The most recent study was conducted by Ermias Kebreab, professor and Sesnon Endowed Chair of the Department of Animal Science and Director of the World Food Center, along with his Ph.D. graduate student Breanna Roque. They found that adding very small amounts of a particular species of red seaweed to beef cattle feed resulted in a comparable weight gain, while the cows burped 82 percent less methane than their herd mates without the seaweed in their diet. In an earlier study, Kebreab and Roque had reduced methane emissions from dairy cows by 50 percent using a different species of red seaweed. Taste-test panels found no differences in the flavor of the meat or in the taste of the milk.[33]

In an interview, Professor Kebreab said, "We now have sound evidence that seaweed in cattle diet is effective at reducing greenhouse gases and that the efficacy does not diminish over time." Scientists are now studying how the needed species of seaweed can be farmed to provide adequate supplies.[34]

Another solution is being offered by the global agricultural supply giant **Cargill, Inc.** The company has announced plans to start selling experimental methane-absorbing wearable masks for cows. Developed in the United Kingdom by **Zelp, Ltd.**, the devices are touted to reduce emissions by more than half. Sander van Zijderveld, Cargill's Strategic Marketing and Technology Lead for West Europe, said the company was attracted to the Zelp device because it could be used in conjunction with other solutions, like the methane-reducing feed additives. The initiative fits with Minneapolis-based Cargill's announced goal of reducing emissions from all of its global supply chains by 30 percent by 2030.[35]

Researchers in Germany have been toilet-training cows in an effort to reduce nitrous oxide emissions—a potent greenhouse gas produced when ammonia in cow urine mixes with soil. The Research

Institute for Farm Biology has found that cows respond well to incentives to use what has been dubbed a "MooLoo" for urination. The urine can then be captured and treated. The study reported, "The calves showed a level of performance comparable to that of children and superior to that of very young children."[36] Practical applications are yet to be fully identified. But the study demonstrated that imaginative solutions to agricultural emissions can be achieved. Researchers also noted that reducing the amount of urine in the cows' pens improves their hygiene and overall welfare.

Despite these innovations, the production of beef and lamb requires about 20 times more land area and generates 20 times more greenhouse gas emissions than plant-based proteins. Therefore, many people are choosing to eat less meat, and plant-based products that mimic meats are becoming more convincing and gaining popularity. Companies like **Impossible Foods** and **Beyond Meat** are developing "plant-based 'beef' that looks, sizzles, tastes, and even bleeds like the real thing."[37]

New technologies are also enabling heavy industries to operate in more environmentally responsible ways. For example, **Pure Earth Plasma Holdings** in North America and **Synergen Met** in Australia are using plasma technologies around the world in the production of hydrogen and carbon black with little to no carbon emissions.

Like solid, liquid, or gas, plasma is a state of matter. Plasma consists of electrons released from their orbits around the nuclei of atoms, freely floating with nuclei and positively charged ions as a result of exposure to high temperatures or high voltage electricity. Because stars are made of plasma, it is the most common state of matter in the universe. Here on Earth, it is created in lightning strikes and fire is classified as a plasma. It is used in televisions, fluorescent and neon lights, and quite a number of manufacturing processes like fine cleaning or surface coating—and now in the production of hydrogen and carbon black.

Hydrogen is used in petroleum refining, fertilizer manufacturing, and fuel cells that generate electricity. Unlike gasoline or diesel-powered vehicles, hydrogen fuel cell-powered vehicles emit no greenhouse gases. But traditional methods of producing the hydrogen do. So, the ability to produce hydrogen with very low-emission technology makes hydrogen fuel cell-powered vehicles a more desirable option.

Carbon black is used in a wide range of products. It makes tires more durable. It is used as pigmentation in paints, ink, laser printer toner and other products. It is added to many kinds of plastics and to electronic components. It is practically ubiquitous, and traditionally very environmentally unfriendly to produce. So, a new way to make it with no emissions is very good news.

Synergen is also using plasma technology to destroy harmful polyfluoroalkyl (PFAS) chemicals found in drinking water among other places. A recent study found that PFAS chemicals have likely tainted "nearly half" of tap water in the United States.[38] These man-made compounds are used to make water-repellant materials, non-stick coatings, carpets, and packaging materials. They are ingredients in fire-suppressant foams that have been widely used for fire-training in factories, refineries, and airfields, where they remain in the soils. PFAS compounds are called "forever chemicals" because they do not break down in the environment. So, using plasma technology to destroy them benefits us all.

As the latest IPCC[*] Report made clear, even if we were able to stop greenhouse gas emissions immediately, the cascading effects of what is already in the atmosphere will continue to cause problems. In addition to that, significant emissions will continue for at least a few decades. Therefore, the development of remediation methods is becoming more and more crucial—methods of extracting CO_2 from the atmosphere.

The restoration of forests and wetlands will do quite a lot to remove carbon dioxide from the atmosphere, but it will not be enough. The capture and storage of vast quantities of the gas are also

---

[*] International Panel on Climate Change at the UN

needed. Current models suggest, to meet the goal of no more than 1.5° C warming by 2100, as set by the Paris Agreement, the sequester of as much as 10 gigatons of CO_2 per year is needed through 2050, and 20 gigatons per year from 2050 to the end of the century.[39]

Currently the carbon dioxide used in industrial applications and soft-drink and beer carbonation is collected from power plant exhausts that have high concentrations of the gas. The exhaust gases are processed to make pure carbon dioxide. Capturing CO_2 from the air, commonly referred to as "direct air capture" (DAC), is much more challenging.

Elon Musk has said he will invest a hundred million dollars in carbon capture technologies. ExxonMobil, Microsoft, United Airlines along with a few other companies are reportedly also investing billions in the endeavor,[40] and prototypes for several methods are being tested. One of the more promising ideas has come from researchers at the Massachusetts Institute of Technology (MIT).

MIT engineers have developed a system that can extract CO_2 from either power plant exhausts or open air, with no by-product to be disposed of and using only a minimum of energy. The system can operate at room temperature and normal air pressure.

The device is essentially a series of electrochemical cells that absorb carbon dioxide from the air when charged. When discharged, the CO_2 is released and contained. The discharge of the gas from the chamber also provides part of the power needed for the system. For continuous operation, as need on exhaust stacks, a dual system can have alternate charge and discharge cycles. An industrial-sized prototype has yet to be constructed, but the technology looks promising.

As DAC systems are developed, the next hurdle is what to do with the collected carbon dioxide. The commercial market for CO_2 is far too small to make a significant impact, so it will have to be stored or disposed of. The most practical solution appears to be injecting the carbon into the geologic formations from which oil and gas have previously been extracted. To have any significant effect on climate, carbon dioxide mitigation will need to be done on a massive scale.

There is currently no financial incentive for storing carbon dioxide. So, it will have to done by governments directly or through incentives imposed by carbon taxes in one form or another. High emission industries could buy offsets in a cap-and-trade scheme, for example. In any case, DAC systems will not be a substitute for cutting emissions, but these new technologies do leave some room for hope that humankind will avert catastrophe.

We can also be encouraged by some of the initiatives that governments and NGOs[*] have engaged in to preserve or restore resources and ecosystems. A pilot program in southern Ecuador, for example, is incentivizing residents of 14 municipalities to work together in an effort to conserve water and protect the regional watershed from deforestation and pollution. The Regional Water Fund of Southern Ecuador has purchased land and made agreements with ranchers to rewild pastures where cattle had been polluting the watershed. Funded by a fee on water consumption amounting to about one dollar per month for the average family, the program has restored 3,700 acres and put 833,000 acres of watershed forests under protection. The group hopes to expand its conservation program to include 1.48 million acres of watershed serving 39 municipalities by 2030.[41]

In 2001, state and federal authorities approved the disposal of decommissioned New York City subway cars in the Atlantic Ocean 16 miles off the coast of Delaware. On the otherwise featureless ocean floor, 80 feet down, lie 714 "Redbird" subway cars; 86 military tanks and armored personnel carriers; 8 tugboats and barges; and 3,000 tons of truck tires. In the 20 years since its installation, the Redbird Reef has become the home of coral, sea mollusks, sponges, barnacles, seahorses, mussels, sea turtles, and a host of other creatures. The new ecosystem has also attracted large game fish and, in turn, fishermen.[42] While not as desirable as natural reefs, artificial

---

[*] Non-profit non-governmental organizations

reefs are helping to mitigate the loss of natural reefs that are essential to the ocean ecosystems upon which the world's fish depend.

In the Netherlands, a national pollinator program is working to stabilize urban bee populations. More than half of that nation's native bee species are endangered as a result of habitat losses. So, bee-friendly habitats were created in urban areas. In Amsterdam, for example, "bee hotels" (structures suitable for bees to find refuge) were erected, and grassy public lands have been replaced with flowering plants for the bees to find nectar. Thousands of volunteers recently participated in the nation's fourth annual bee census, when they counted and identified the various bee and hoverfly species in their gardens. The findings showed the program has been working to help stabilize most populations of the Netherlands' essential pollinators.[43]

With financial and technical support from the World Bank, Uganda's second-largest city, Jinja, has begun installing solar-powered street lights. Since they are self-contained, the new lights are 25 percent less expensive to install than traditional street lights. Their maintenance has proved to be 60 percent less costly too. The more reliable lights have saved energy, increased safety, and allowed businesses to thrive by staying open into the evenings.[44] The program has shown that new technologies can reduce carbon emissions while improving people's lives.

Palm oil is a remarkably useful and very versatile substance. It is used in nearly half of all packaged products found in the supermarket—from a wide variety of food products to cosmetics. Because of its usefulness, it is very profitable to produce. Native to Africa, palm oil trees have been transported to and are grown in 44 countries, including Indonesia and Malaysia where more than 85 percent of the global supply of palm oil is produced. To make room for palm oil trees, vast tracts of some of the world's most important and biodiverse forests in Indonesia and Malaysia have been destroyed—forests that include the homes of endangered species like the Orangutan, the pygmy elephant, and the Sumatran rhino. As a result, Indonesia has now adopted policies to stem the loss of its forests, as well as to protect its carbon-absorbing mangroves and peatlands. With a temporary ban on new palm oil plantations, deforestation there has declined for the last four years. It is a small, but crucial step in protecting the third-largest and one of the world's most important tropical forests.[45]

Since the 1970s, a "green cities movement" of conservation-minded cities and towns has spread around the world. A growing number of urban areas are working to encourage the development of more densely compacted housing, pedestrian friendly business districts, public transportation, and natural open spaces, in efforts to reduce waste and lower emissions. We are also seeing trends in American suburbs where developers are creating "town squares," in which high-density housing is set above restaurants and retail shops with easy access to parks and hike-and-bike trails. Residents can live, shop, dine, and play without the need of a car.

When architect and urban planner Jamie Lerner became mayor of Curitiba, Brazil in 1972, he closed six blocks of the city's central business district to cars. The pedestrian-only district soon became popular with businesses and residents. Now, the car-free district has grown three times larger and serves as the heart of a prosperous metropolis.

Lerner also encouraged high-density housing development around public transit hubs, while leaving abundant open space and forest around the city. Today, some three-quarters of the area's 3.2 million residents regularly use the modern public transportation system, with little need of a car.[46] The metropolis emits about 25 percent less carbon per capita than most other Brazilian cities, despite higher car ownership.

The city of Reykjavik, Iceland has received funding from the European Union to acquire buses powered by hydrogen fuel cells for its public transit system. The new buses can operate for a full day before refueling, as opposed to the electric buses currently in use, which need to be recharged after only a half day of operation.[47] Despite its abundant need for energy to heat homes and businesses, 100 percent of Iceland's electricity and structure-heating needs are met with renewable sources—primarily geothermal and hydro-power. Iceland intends to be completely carbon neutral by 2040.

In 2005, Portland, Oregon was the first U.S. city to meet the CO_2 emission goals of the Kyoto Protocol. Seattle, Washington is collaborating with 590 other U.S. cities under the U.S. Mayors Climate Protection Agreement in an effort to meet that same goal. The cities of Vancouver, British Columbia and Austin, Texas received praise for preserving open spaces. Many cities and counties are now requiring stricter standards of energy efficiency in both commercial and residential building codes.

There is no formal green cities mandate or organization, but groups like **GreenCities Events** and **International Sustainable Solutions** offer opportunities for collaboration and provide information to help cities achieve sustainability goals.[48] The U.S. Environmental Protection Agency also promotes the greening of cities by providing urban designers, planners, and consultants in conjunction with other U.S. federal agencies.[49] Through public and private partnerships, both out of necessity and by popular demand, a great many of the world's cities are going green.

Much of what we have seen in previous chapters of this book may seem a bit bleak and pessimistic. It should. There is plenty to be concerned about—not just the destruction of the ecosystems upon which we depend and the wildlife and landscapes we cherish, but also the wars and the political strife that will inevitably result from resource shortages. But, perhaps all is not yet lost. As we have seen in this chapter, there is at least some reason for hope, reason to believe humanity just might be able to avert catastrophe. We can preserve the beauty and riches of our world if we choose to do so, and a great many people are choosing to do their part.

While there is room for hope, there remains much to be done. With roughly half of the political power structure in the United States preoccupied by its "culture wars," its skepticism of science, and its divisive use of ethnocentric proclivities in a quest for power, the political climate desperately needs to be mended. Electing public servants who are committed to focusing on long-term solutions to our environmental and social justice problems will go a long way toward restoring a healthy two-party political system.

As our founding fathers repeatedly emphasized, a healthy democracy is dependent upon a well-informed electorate. That is why objective journalism is so important. It also why we need to be able to recognize propaganda and disinformation.

A lot is being written about climate change and other environmental issues of our time, and more and more people are coming to recognize the urgency of those concerns. Once the political momentum has sufficiently turned toward the long-term interests of the electorate and the world, the disinformation may begin to subside. Radio and television personalities may then be forced to find a market share among people who recognize their own interests are synonymous with those of a wider world, not just their own favored faction, however they might imagine it.

With the election of President Joe Biden, the political momentum has shifted slightly toward a more sustainable world. But the direction is tentative. It remains vulnerable to disinformation and indifference. It will only be when dishonesty and unreason are thoroughly and repeatedly rejected by the electorate that political momentum will allow the world to do what is needed.

A resurgence of public support for family-planning programs around the world will go a long way toward empowering women, reducing poverty, and reducing the environmental impact of population growth. Family planning in conjunction with anti-poverty initiatives will enable people to live more environmentally responsible lives.

Education and better enforcement of poaching laws along with habitat protections will help to save many of the most threatened species. Better awareness of what is being lost with reckless deforestation will preserve species and could eventually help to reduce the amount of carbon dioxide in the atmosphere.

Most economists agree that carbon taxes along with cap-and-trade schemes are the best way to incentivize moving from carbon-based energy sources to renewable and sustainable sources without unduly hindering our free enterprise system. Europe has already taken the lead; The United States and the rest of the world will need to catch up. Carbon tariffs will provide incentives for exporting countries to do their part. Carbon taxes, carbon checks, carbon tariffs and other schemes can take many forms. We need not describe all the possibilities here. We need only to be open to doing our part in adopting or supporting solutions.

Ultimately, it is up to each of us as individuals to support green public initiatives and to manage our personal preferences and behavior in ways that preserve the planet for future generations.

With our many discoveries, inventions, innovations, and great expansion of knowledge, humankind has created a wonderful time to be alive for most people—a great Anthropocene epoch. It stands to reason, therefore, that we are ultimately capable of propagating knowledge, relieving suffering, and enabling prosperity throughout the world. There can be no reasonable doubt that we have a moral obligation to do all that we can to create a sustainable and prosperous world for all its people and their children.

Surely, we have the capacity to preserve our planet for the benefit of many generations to come, if we simply choose to do so.

*   *   *   *

Endangered Species

M ore than 37,400 species of animals and plants are known to be threatened with extinction. Scientists say there are perhaps a million others that have yet to be identified (mostly in tropical rain forests). Below are a few of the most familiar animals. When these creatures are lost, the richness of our world will surely be diminished.

COMMON NAME	CONSERVATION STATUS
Amur Leopard	Critically Endangered
Black Rhinoceros	Critically Endangered
Bornean Orangutan	Critically Endangered
Cross River Gorilla	Critically Endangered
Eastern Lowland Gorilla	Critically Endangered
Hawksbill Sea Turtle	Critically Endangered
Javan Rhinoceros	Critically Endangered
Kemp's Ridley Sea Turtle	Critically Endangered
Sumatran Elephant	Critically Endangered
Sumatran Orangutan	Critically Endangered
Sumatran Rhinoceros	Critically Endangered
Sunda Tiger	Critically Endangered
Vaquita	Critically Endangered
Western Lowland Gorilla	Critically Endangered
Yangtze Finless Porpoise	Critically Endangered
African Wild Dog	Endangered
Asian Elephant	Endangered
Black-footed Ferret	Endangered
Blue Whale	Endangered
Bluefin Tuna	Endangered
Bonobo	Endangered
Bornean Elephant	Endangered
Chimpanzee	Endangered

Fin Whale	Endangered
Galápagos Penguin	Endangered
Ganges River Dolphin	Endangered
Green Sea Turtle	Endangered
Hector's Dolphin	Endangered
Indus River Dolphin	Endangered
Irrawaddy Dolphin	Endangered
Mountain Gorilla	Endangered
North Atlantic Right Whale	Endangered
Red Panda	Endangered
Sea Lions	Endangered
Sei Whale	Endangered
Sri Lankan Elephant	Endangered
Tiger (all subspecies)	Endangered
Whale (6 out of 13 great whale species)	Endangered
Whale Shark	Endangered
Austin Blind Salamander	Endangered
Barton Springs Salamander	Endangered
California Condor	Endangered
Crested Honeycreeper	Endangered
Cape Sable Seaside Sparrow	Endangered
Florida Grasshopper Sparrow	Endangered
Hawaiian Crow	Endangered
Houston Toad	Endangered
Ivory-billed Woodpecker	Endangered
Laysan Duck	Endangered
Masked Bobwhite Quail	Endangered
Mississippi Sandhill Crane	Endangered
Nightingale Reed Warbler	Endangered
Northern Aplomado Falcon	Endangered
Puerto Rican Broad-winged Hawk	Endangered
Puerto Rican Parrot	Endangered
Red-cockaded Woodpecker	Endangered
Southern Willow Flycatcher	Endangered
Thick-billed Parrot	Endangered
White-necked Crow	Endangered
Whooping Crane	Endangered

Wyoming Toad	Endangered
Yellow-shouldered Blackbird	Endangered
Alabama Pearlshell Clam	Endangered
California Freshwater Shrimp	Endangered
Nashville Crayfish	Endangered
Longhorn Fairy Shrimp	Endangered
Alabama Sturgeon	Endangered
Atlantic Salmon (Gulf of Maine)	Endangered
Leon Springs Pupfish	Endangered
Rio Grande Silvery Minnow	Endangered
White Sturgeon	Endangered
Bartram's Hairstreak Butterfly	Endangered
Behren's Silverspot Butterfly	Endangered
Callipe Silverspot Butterfly	Endangered
Casey's June Beetle	Endangered
Crimson Hawaiian Damselfly	Endangered
El Segundo Blue Butterfly	Endangered
Florida Leafwing Butterfly	Endangered
Karner Blue Butterfly	Endangered
Mariana Eight-spot Butterfly	Endangered
Miami Blue Butterfly	Endangered
Miami Tiger Beetle	Endangered
Mount Charleston Blue Butterfly	Endangered
Rusty Patch Bumble Bee	Endangered
Salt Creek Tiger Beetle	Endangered
Carolina Northern Flying Squirrel	Endangered
Columbia Basin Pygmy Rabbit	Endangered
Florida Panther	Endangered
Fresno Kangaroo Rat	Endangered
Key Deer	Endangered
Little Mariana Fruit Bat	Endangered
Lower Keys Marsh Rabbit	Endangered
Mexican Long-nosed Bat	Endangered
Mexican Wolf	Endangered
New Mexico Meadow Jumping Mouse	Endangered
Point Arena Mountain Beaver	Endangered
Red Wolf	Endangered

Riparian Brush Rabbit	Endangered
San Joaquin Kit Fox	Endangered
Sierra Nevada Bighorn Sheep	Endangered
Sinaloan Jaguarundi	Endangered
Sonoran Pronghorn	Endangered
Alabama Red-bellied Turtle	Endangered
Loggerhead Sea Turtle (North Pacific Ocean)	Endangered
Leatherback Sea Turtle	Endangered
Plymouth Red-bellied Turtle	Endangered
African Elephant	Vulnerable
Bigeye Tuna	Vulnerable
Black Spider Monkey	Vulnerable
Forest Elephant	Vulnerable
Giant Panda	Vulnerable
Giant Tortoise	Vulnerable
Great White Shark	Vulnerable
Greater One-Horned Rhinoceros	Vulnerable
Hippopotamus	Vulnerable
Leatherback Turtle	Vulnerable
Lion	Vulnerable
Loggerhead Turtle	Vulnerable
Marine Iguana	Vulnerable
Olive Ridley Turtle	Vulnerable
Polar Bear	Vulnerable
Savanna Elephant	Vulnerable
Snow Leopard	Vulnerable
Southern Rockhopper Penguin	Vulnerable
Northern Sea Otter	Threatened
Southern Sea Otter	Threatened
Wood Bison	Threatened
Albacore Tuna	Near Threatened
Beluga Whale	Near Threatened
Greater Sage-Grouse	Near Threatened
Jaguar	Near Threatened
Plains Bison	Near Threatened
White Rhino	Near Threatened
Yellowfin Tuna	Near Threatened

Our Carbon Footprint*

T he term "carbon footprint" refers to the amount of greenhouse gas (GHG) emissions produced directly or indirectly by the existence and activities of an individual person, an organization, a facility, an event, or a product.[1] The carbon footprint of an entity is calculated by totaling the GHG emissions produced at all stages of its existence (production materials, manufacturing processes, uses, activities, consumption, and/or end-of-life). Throughout its existence and activity, different GHGs might be emitted, such as carbon dioxide, methane, and nitrous oxide, each with its own greenhouse effect characteristic. The different characteristics are accounted for by each gas's heat-trapping properties being measured as "carbon dioxide equivalents" (CO_2e), making a single unit of measure for easier comparisons. For example, the typical American household emits all of those greenhouse gases, but can be said to have a carbon footprint of 48 metric tons of CO_2e per year.[2]

Below are some statistics and comparisons of the greenhouse gas emissions that we, as individuals, produce in our daily lives. Included are suggestions for how each of us can reduce our own carbon footprints, as well as how we can conserve resources and reduce pollution and landfill waste.

Household Emissions

- For each kilowatt-hour of electricity generated in the U.S., an average of 0.953 pounds of CO_2e is released at the power plant.[3] Coal releases 2.2 pounds, petroleum releases 1.9 pounds, and

---

* The information in this addendum was derived primarily from the "Carbon Footprint Factsheet," Pub. No. CSS09-05, of the *Center for Sustainable Systems* at the University of Michigan (2020).

natural gas releases 0.9 pounds. Nuclear, solar, wind, and hydroelectric release no CO_2 when they produce electricity, but emissions are released during upstream production activities (e.g., manufacture of solar cells, nuclear fuels, cement production, etc.).[4,5]

- U.S residential electricity use in 2018 emitted 666.5 million metric tons of CO_2e.[6]
- Residential heating and cooling are estimated to account for 44 percent of energy use in American homes in 2020.[7]
- In 2015, an average of 720.5 pounds of CO_2e per household was due to household refrigerators.[8]
- Clothes washers in the U.S. emit 26 million metric tons of CO_2e each year. Switching to cold-water washes reduces emissions.[9]

Personal Transportation Emissions

- U.S. fuel economy (mpg) declined by 12 percent from 1987-2004, then improved by 30 percent from 2004-2018, reaching an average of 25.1 mpg in 2018.[10] Annual per capita miles driven increased 9 percent since 1995 to 9,919 miles in 2018.[11]
- Cars and light trucks emitted 1.1 billion metric tons of CO_2e, or 17 percent of the total U.S. GHG emissions, in 2018.[12]
- Of the roughly 66,000 pounds of CO_2e emitted over the lifetime of an internal combustion engine car (assuming 93,000 miles driven), 84 percent come from the use phase (not the manufacturing and disposal phases).[13]
- Gasoline releases 19.6 pounds of CO_2 per gallon when burned, compared to 22.4 pounds per gallon for diesel.[14] However, diesel has 11 percent more BTU per gallon, which improves its fuel economy.[15]
- The average passenger car emits 0.78 pounds of CO_2 per mile driven.[16]
- Automobile fuel economy can improve 7-14 percent by simply observing the speed limit. Every 5 mph increase in vehicle speed

over 50 mph is equivalent to paying an extra $0.13-$0.25 per gallon of gasoline.[17]

- Commercial aircraft emissions in 2018 totaled 130.8 million metric tons of CO_2e. In 2018, the average domestic commercial flight emitted 0.39 pounds of CO_2e per passenger mile.[18]
- In 2018, rail transportation emitted 42.9 million metric tons of CO_2e, making up 2 percent of transportation emissions in the U.S.[19]

Emissions Associated with Food

- The food we consume accounts for 10-30 percent of our households' carbon footprint, with the higher percentages in lower-income households.[20]
- Production of food accounts for 68 percent of its emissions, while transportation accounts for 5 percent.[21]
- Agricultural food production primarily emits CO_2 (carbon dioxide), N_2O (nitrous oxide), and CH_4 (methane).
- Meat products have much larger carbon footprints than vegetables because of the transformation of plant matter into the meat of animals that emit carbon dioxide and methane.
- Ruminants, such as cattle, sheep, and goats, produced 178 million metric tons of CO_2e of enteric methane in the U.S. in 2018.[22]
- The transportation of food to the average household emits the equivalent of driving 1,000 miles. Switching from meat to a vegetarian diet only one day per week would save the equivalent of driving 1,160 miles.[23]
- A vegetarian diet greatly reduced a person's carbon footprint. Switching to less carbon-intensive meats can also reduce an individual's carbon footprint. For example, the carbon footprint of beef is 7.2 times greater than that of chicken.[24]

What We Can Do

For those of us who live in single-family homes with lawns and gardens, there is a lot to consider. We can make an effort to use native plants, which will reduce water consumption and the need for fertilizers and support local pollinators and other wildlife. Using native plants and mulch also reduces the need for insecticides and herbicides. We can use a mulching mower to reduce waste and to put nutrients back into the soil. We can be careful that the fertilizers we use do not run off of the property, where they will eventually make their way into streams, rivers, and the sea. We can better manage our sprinkler systems to reduce water waste.

We can also manage our personal habits, consumption, and diets to reduce our personal carbon footprint. Many of us, mostly young people, are already making environmentally conscious choices by recycling and composting, opting for electronic rather than paper transactions, conserving water, using only LED lighting, buying local to reduce transportation pollution, buying from green companies with a minimum of packaging, carpooling or using mass transit, avoiding food waste, and by reducing meat consumption.

We need not necessarily all go vegan, but we should at least be aware that meat products, especially beef, have a much larger carbon footprint per calorie than grain or vegetables. As we saw above, research has shown that switching to a vegetarian meal only one day per week for a year could save the equivalent of driving 1,160 miles.[25]

There are also some small steps we can take to help. Keeping your car's tires fully inflated, for example, to save fuel. Unplug or turn off appliances and electronic devices (rather than sleep mode) to save energy. We can even look for companies that publish the carbon footprint of their products, and buy accordingly.

Carbon Footprint Calculators

Here are two websites that provide carbon calculators for personal and household greenhouse gas emissions:

The U.S. Environmental Protection Agency:
www.3.epa.gov/carbon-footprint-calculator/

The Nature Conservancy:
www.nature.org/greenliving/carboncalculator/

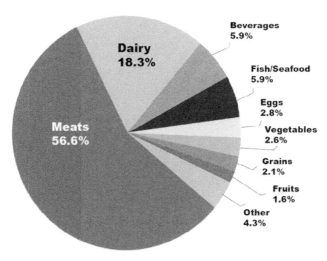

Greenhouse Gases Contribution by Food Type in Average Diet.[26]

The Green New Deal

I n February, 2019, New York Representative Alexandria Ocasio-Cortez and Massachusetts Senator Edward Markey released a fourteen-page document that would be the basis for House Resolution 109 and Senate Resolution 59 calling for a "Green New Deal." Since the House Resolution has been widely discussed and often misrepresented and vilified by some, it might be useful to actually read it. The 116th Congress' House Resolution 109 can be seen in its entirety below.

The Green New Deal Resolution does not include specific policy proposals. Rather, it provides a set of general goals. Its name is a tribute to President Franklin Roosevelt's "New Deal" initiatives that were intended to bring the nation out of the Great Depression and to relieve the suffering of people living in poverty. While not all of the New Deal programs were successful, the long-term result of the overall endeavor was to bring a great many people out of poverty and provide them with basic utilities, stabilize the U.S. economy and, most significantly, strengthen and enlarge the great American middle class, thus benefiting all Americans.

In the case of the Green New Deal, the overall goal is to advocate for American and world economies that meet today's challenges—to create a sustainable world, in which all peoples can prosper.

One of the more common criticisms of the Green New Deal is that the resolution includes commentary on matters of economic and social justice. The accusation is that the resolution contains a "Democrat wish list of hand-outs" in a document purported to speak to the issues of the environment and climate change. Such criticism, however, overlooks the ways in which economic justice and environmental preservation are linked. Inclusive and cohesive societies are the most capable of meeting the greatest challenges. Societies that discount social justice and embrace an everyone-for-themselves way of thinking are limited to prosperity for very few people at the expense of most, with little thought or progress toward a sustainable future. (Note the corrupt countries of Southeast Asia, Latin America, and Africa.) As was clearly demonstrated with President Roosevelt's New Deal initiatives, lifting the prospects of the most vulnerable people enhances the prospects of everyone.

The Green New Deal resolution does not, as some proclaim, advocate taking away our SUVs. Most of what is needed to meet its goals can be achieved with incentives, not mandates. Though mandates imposed on some industries are inevitable, many companies will welcome them, since mandates can often be helpful to those companies that wish to compete on a "level playing field." Mandates can prevent competitors from having a corrupt advantage.

Given that the Resolution only speaks of goals, how those goals will be met, modified, or ignored will be played out in the political processes of the United States Congress. It is unquestionably ambitious—some have said, naïve. But should we not, at the very least, aspire to prosperity and justice for all people in a sustainable world?

116TH CONGRESS 1ST SESSION

H. RES. 109

Recognizing the duty of the Federal Government to create a Green New Deal.

IN THE HOUSE OF REPRESENTATIVES

FEBRUARY 7, 2019

Ms. OCASIO-CORTEZ (for herself, Mr. HASTINGS, Ms. TLAIB, Mr. SERRANO, Mrs. CAROLYN B. MALONEY of New York, Mr. VARGAS, Mr. ESPAILLAT, Mr. LYNCH, Ms. VELA′ZQUEZ, Mr. BLUMENAUER, Mr. BRENDAN F. BOYLE of Pennsylvania, Mr. CASTRO of Texas, Ms. CLARKE of New York, Ms. JAYAPAL, Mr. KHANNA, Mr. TED LIEU of California, Ms. PRESSLEY, Mr. WELCH, Mr. ENGEL, Mr. NEGUSE, Mr.

NADLER, Mr. MCGOVERN, Mr. POCAN, Mr. TAKANO, Ms. NORTON, Mr. RASKIN, Mr. CONNOLLY, Mr. LOWENTHAL, Ms. MATSUI, Mr. THOMPSON of California, Mr. LEVIN of California, Ms. PINGREE, Mr. QUIGLEY, Mr. HUFFMAN, Mrs. WATSON COLEMAN, Mr. GARC´IA of Illinois, Mr. HIGGINS of New York, Ms. HAALAND, Ms. MENG, Mr. CARBAJAL, Mr. CICILLINE, Mr. COHEN, Ms. CLARK of Massachusetts, Ms. JUDY CHU of California, Ms. MUCARSEL-POWELL, Mr. MOULTON, Mr. GRIJALVA, Mr. MEEKS, Mr. SABLAN, Ms. LEE of California, Ms. BONAMICI, Mr. SEAN PATRICK MALONEY of New York, Ms. SCHAKOWSKY, Ms. DELAURO, Mr. LEVIN of Michigan, Ms. MCCOLLUM, Mr. DESAULNIER, Mr. COURTNEY, Mr. LARSON of Connecticut, Ms. ESCOBAR, Mr. SCHIFF, Mr. KEATING, Mr. DEFAZIO, Ms. ESHOO, Mrs. TRAHAN, Mr. GOMEZ, Mr. KENNEDY, and Ms. WATERS) submitted the following resolution; which was referred to the Committee on Energy and Commerce, and in addition to the Committees on Science, Space, and Technology, Education and Labor, Transportation and Infrastructure, Agriculture, Natural Resources, Foreign Affairs, Financial Services, the Judiciary, Ways and Means, and Oversight and Reform, for a period to be subsequently determined by the Speaker, in each case for consideration of such provisions as fall within the jurisdiction of the committee concerned.

RESOLUTION

Whereas the October 2018 report entitled "Special Report on Global Warming of 1.5° C" by the Intergovernmental Panel on Climate Change and the November 2018 Fourth National Climate Assessment report found that—

(1) human activity is the dominant cause of observed climate change over the past century;

(2) a changing climate is causing sea levels to rise and an increase in wildfires, severe storms, droughts, and other extreme weather events that threaten human life, healthy communities, and critical infrastructure;

(3) global warming at or above 2 degrees Celsius beyond pre-industrialized levels will cause—

(A) mass migration from the regions most affected by climate change;

(B) more than $500,000,000,000 in lost annual economic output in the United States by the year 2100;

(C) wildfires that, by 2050, will annually burn at least twice as much forest area in the western United States than was typically burned by wildfires in the years preceding 2019;

(D) a loss of more than 99 percent of all coral reefs on Earth;

(E) more than 350,000,000 more people to be exposed globally to deadly heat stress by 2050; and

(F) a risk of damage to $1,000,000,000,000 of public infrastructure and coastal real estate in the United States; and

(4) global temperatures must be kept below 1.5 degrees Celsius above pre-industrialized levels to avoid the most severe impacts of a changing climate, which will require—
(A) global reductions in greenhouse gas emissions from human sources of 40 to 60 percent from 2010 levels by 2030; and
(B) net-zero global emissions by 2050;

Whereas, because the United States has historically been responsible for a disproportionate amount of greenhouse gas emissions, having emitted 20 percent of global greenhouse gas emissions through 2014, and has a high technological capacity, the United States must take a leading role in reducing emissions through economic transformation;

Whereas the United States is currently experiencing several related crises, with—

(1) life expectancy declining while basic needs, such as clean air, clean water, healthy food, and adequate health care, housing, transportation, and education, are inaccessible to a significant portion of the United States population;

(2) a 4-decade trend of wage stagnation, deindustrialization, and antilabor policies that has led to—
(A) hourly wages overall stagnating since the 1970s despite increased worker productivity;
(B) the third-worst level of socioeconomic mobility in the developed world before the Great Recession;
(C) the erosion of the earning and bargaining power of workers in the United States; and
(D) inadequate resources for public sector workers to confront the challenges of climate change at local, State, and Federal levels; and

(3) the greatest income inequality since the 1920s, with—
(A) the top 1 percent of earners accruing 91 percent of gains in the first few years of economic recovery after the Great Recession;
(B) a large racial wealth divide amounting to a difference of 20 times more wealth between the average white family and the average black family; and
(C) a gender earnings gap that results in women earning approximately 80 percent as much as men, at the median;

Whereas climate change, pollution, and environmental destruction have exacerbated systemic racial, regional, social, environmental, and economic injustices (referred to in this preamble as "systemic injustices") by disproportionately affecting indigenous peoples, communities of color, migrant communities, deindustrialized communities, depopulated rural communities, the poor, low-income workers, women, the elderly, the unhoused, people with disabilities, and youth (referred to in this preamble as "frontline and vulnerable communities");

Whereas, climate change constitutes a direct threat to the national security of the United States—

(1) by impacting the economic, environmental, and social stability of countries and communities around the world; and

(2) by acting as a threat multiplier;

Whereas the Federal Government-led mobilizations during World War II and the New Deal created the greatest middle class that the United States has ever seen, but many members of frontline and vulnerable communities were excluded from many of the economic and societal benefits of those mobilizations; and

Whereas the House of Representatives recognizes that a new national, social, industrial, and economic mobilization on a scale not seen since World War II and the New Deal era is a historic opportunity—

(1) to create millions of good, high-wage jobs in the United States;

(2) to provide unprecedented levels of prosperity and economic security for all people of the United States; and

(3) to counteract systemic injustices

Now, therefore, be it *Resolved,* that it is the sense of the House of Representatives that—

(1) it is the duty of the Federal Government to create a Green New Deal—
(A) to achieve net-zero greenhouse gas emissions through a fair and just transition for all communities and workers;
(B) to create millions of good, high-wage jobs and ensure prosperity and economic security for all people of the United States;
(C) to invest in the infrastructure and industry of the United States to sustainably meet the challenges of the 21st century;

(D) to secure for all people of the United States for generations to come—

(i) clean air and water;

(ii) climate and community resiliency;

(iii) healthy food;

(iv) access to nature; and

(v) a sustainable environment; and

(E) to promote justice and equity by stopping current, preventing future, and repairing historic oppression of indigenous peoples, communities of color, migrant communities, deindustrialized communities, depopulated rural communities, the poor, low-income workers, women, the elderly, the unhoused, people with disabilities, and youth (referred to in this resolution as "frontline and vulnerable communities"):

(2) the goals described in subparagraphs (A) through (E) of paragraph (1) (referred to in this resolution as the "Green New Deal goals") should be accomplished through a 10-year national mobilization (referred to in this resolution as the "Green New Deal mobilization") that will require the following goals and projects—

(A) building resiliency against climate change-related disasters, such as extreme weather, including by leveraging funding and providing investments for community-defined projects and strategies;

(B) repairing and upgrading the infrastructure in the United States, including—

(i) by eliminating pollution and greenhouse gas emissions as much as technologically feasible;

(ii) by guaranteeing universal access to clean water;

(iii) by reducing the risks posed by climate impacts; and

(iv) by ensuring that any infrastructure bill considered by Congress addresses climate change;

(C) meeting 100 percent of the power demand in the United States through clean, renewable, and zero-emission energy sources, including—

(i) by dramatically expanding and upgrading renewable power sources; and

(ii) by deploying new capacity;

(D) building or upgrading to energy-efficient, distributed, and "smart" power grids, and ensuring affordable access to electricity;

(E) upgrading all existing buildings in the United States and building new buildings to achieve maximum energy efficiency, water efficiency, safety, affordability, comfort, and durability, including through electrification;

(F) spurring massive growth in clean manufacturing in the United States and removing pollution and greenhouse gas emissions from manufacturing and industry as much as is technologically feasible, including by expanding renewable energy manufacturing and investing in existing manufacturing and industry;

(G) working collaboratively with farmers and ranchers in the United States to remove pollution and greenhouse gas emissions from the agricultural sector as much as is technologically feasible, including—

(i) by supporting family farming;

(ii) by investing in sustainable farming and land use practices that increase soil health; and

(iii) by building a more sustainable food system that ensures universal access to healthy food;

(H) overhauling transportation systems in the United States to remove pollution and greenhouse gas emissions from the transportation sector as much as is technologically feasible, including through investment in—

(i) zero-emission vehicle infrastructure and manufacturing;

(ii) clean, affordable, and accessible public transit; and

(iii) high-speed rail;

(I) mitigating and managing the long-term adverse health, economic, and other effects of pollution and climate change, including by pro- viding funding for community-defined projects and strategies;

(J) removing greenhouse gases from the atmosphere and reducing pollution by restoring natural ecosystems through proven low-tech solutions that increase soil carbon storage, such as land preservation and afforestation;

(K) restoring and protecting threatened, endangered, and fragile ecosystems through locally appropriate and science-based projects that enhance biodiversity and support climate resiliency;

(L) cleaning up existing hazardous waste and abandoned sites, ensuring economic development and sustainability on those sites;

(M) identifying other emission and pollution sources and creating solutions to remove them; and

(N) promoting the international exchange of technology, expertise, products, funding, and services, with the aim of making the United States the international leader on climate action, and to help other countries achieve a Green New Deal;

(3) a Green New Deal must be developed through transparent and inclusive consultation, collaboration, and partnership with frontline and vulnerable communities, labor unions, worker cooperatives, civil society groups, academia, and businesses; and

(4) to achieve the Green New Deal goals and mobilization, a Green New Deal will require the following goals and projects—

(A) providing and leveraging, in a way that ensures that the public receives appropriate ownership stakes and returns on investment, adequate capital (including through community grants, public banks, and other public financing), technical expertise, supporting policies, and other forms of assistance to communities, organizations, Federal, State, and local government agencies, and businesses working on the Green New Deal mobilization;

(B) ensuring that the Federal Government takes into account the complete environmental and social costs and impacts of emissions through—

(i) existing laws;

(ii) new policies and programs; and

(iii) ensuring that frontline and vulnerable communities shall not be adversely affected;

(C) providing resources, training, and high-quality education, including higher education, to all people of the United States, with a focus on frontline and vulnerable communities, so that all people of the United States may be full and equal participants in the Green New Deal mobilization;

(D) making public investments in the research and development of new clean and renewable energy technologies and industries;

(E) directing investments to spur economic development, deepen and diversify industry and business in local and regional economies, and build wealth and community ownership, while prioritizing high-quality job creation and economic, social, and environmental benefits in frontline and vulnerable communities, and deindustrialized communities, that may otherwise struggle with the transition away from greenhouse gas intensive industries;

(F) ensuring the use of democratic and participatory processes that are inclusive of and led by frontline and vulnerable communities and workers to plan, implement, and administer the Green New Deal mobilization at the local level;

(G) ensuring that the Green New Deal mobilization creates high-quality union jobs that pay prevailing wages, hires local workers, offers training and advancement opportunities, and guarantees wage and benefit parity for workers affected by the transition;

(H) guaranteeing a job with a family-sustaining wage, adequate family and medical leave, paid vacations, and retirement security to all people of the United States;

(I) strengthening and protecting the right of all workers to organize, unionize, and collectively bargain free of coercion, intimidation, and harassment;

(J) strengthening and enforcing labor, workplace health and safety, antidiscrimination, and wage and hour standards across all employers, industries, and sectors;

(K) enacting and enforcing trade rules, procurement standards, and border adjustments with strong labor and environmental protections—

             (i) to stop the transfer of jobs and pollution overseas; and

             (ii) to grow domestic manufacturing in the United States;

(L) ensuring that public lands, waters, and oceans are protected and that eminent domain is not abused;

(M) obtaining the free, prior, and informed consent of indigenous peoples for all decisions that affect indigenous peoples and their traditional territories, honoring all treaties and agreements with indigenous peoples, and protecting and enforcing the sovereignty and land rights of indigenous peoples;

(N) ensuring a commercial environment where every businessperson is free from unfair competition and domination by domestic or international monopolies; and

(O) providing all people of the United States with—

             (i) high-quality health care;

             (ii) affordable, safe, and adequate housing;

             (iii) economic security; and

             (iv) access to clean water, clean air, healthy and affordable food, and to nature.

Additional Reading

Life: A Natural History of the First Four Billion Years of Life on Earth, by Richard Fortey. The title well describes this wonderful book.

Transcendence: How Humans Evolved Through Fire, Language, Beauty, and Time, by Gaia Vince. One of the best books available on cultural evolution. It well explains how we came to be who we are.

A Short History of Nearly Everything, by Bill Bryson. This marvelously entertaining book is informative of, well, nearly everything about the natural world in which we live.

The Sixth Extinction: An Unnatural History, by Elizabeth Kolbert. In this Pulitzer Prize-winning book, Kolbert takes readers into the work of scientists endeavoring to better understand what has been lost and the threats facing the world's remaining creatures.

The Wizard and the Prophet: Two Remarkable Scientists and Their Dueling Visions to Shape Tomorrow's World, by Charles C. Mann. This is the compelling and masterfully told tale of two scientists with competing visions of how best to feed our growing population.

Adventures in the Anthropocene: A Journey to the Heart of the Planet We Made, by science journalist Gaia Vince. Vince takes us to remote and fascinating places around the world to see what people are doing to cope with our changing planet.

The War on Science: Who's Waging It, Why It Matters, What We Can Do About It, by Shawn Otto, describes the ongoing battle between science and factional interests—between the truth and the powerful. It explains the psychology and the cultural trends that lead many of us to be fooled into rejecting objective science.

Silent Spring, by Rachel Carson. Originally published in 1962, this landmark book brought awareness of the hazards of toxic chemicals and pollution. As the book's message reverberated throughout the world, it helped to usher in the environmental movement.

The Silk Roads, by Peter Frankopan, describes the history of human civilization from the perspective of the trade practices and routes of Southwest Asia (the cradle of civilization) with thorough and engaging prose.

The Columbian Exchange: Biological and Cultural Consequences of 1492, by Alfred W. Crosby Jr.

The Song of the Dodo: Island Biogeography in an Age of Extinctions, by David Quammen. From its beginning, this elegant work engages readers with the what and the why of species extinctions, while marveling at the world's magnificent creatures.

The Ferocious Summer: Adelie Penguins and the Warming of Antarctica, by Meredith Hooper. In delightful prose, Hooper engages readers with her love of Antarctica and its living creatures.

The Uninhabitable Earth: Life After Warming, by David Wells-Wallace. A sobering look at the challenges ahead.

The Living Planet Report is published bi-annually by the World Wildlife Fund and the Zoological Society of London. The free publication is available online and "is a comprehensive study of trends in global biodiversity and the health of the planet." Within the report is the *Living Planet Index*, provided by the Zoological Society of London, which reports on the monitoring of wildlife populations around the world.

Acknowledgements

There is an old adage in academia that wryly proclaims, "To use the work of another person is plagiarism, but to use the work of many is scholarship." While I make no claim of scholarship, I must express my enormous gratitude to the many people upon whose work I have drawn to assemble the information and ideas in this book—most particularly, the journalists who do the very hard work of research and interviews with the scientists and others who well understand the issues of our day. I also wish to thank those research scientists who persist in discovering the truth of our world, many of whom work within government agencies that very often experience too little public support.

I want to recognize the National Geographic Society and the World Wildlife Fund for their magnificent work, a portion of which I have drawn upon for this volume. These non-profits, among a few others, are indispensable to the crucial task of increasing public awareness of the environmental challenges facing our world.

I am very grateful to my editor, Eva Shaw, for her invaluable input. Her masterful understanding of the English language and her thoughtful attention to detail was most helpful.

And finally, I thank my wife Ginny for her help with graphics and the manuscript. Most importantly, I am grateful for her love and faithful support of all my disparate pursuits.

About the Author

B ruce Glass is a businessman, artist, and author. For more than thirty years he has been engaged in the business of commercial photography, traveling for assignments throughout much of the United States. *The Anthropocene Epoch* is Mr. Glass' second book. His first, *Exploring Faith and Reason: The Reconciliation of Christianity and Biological Evolution* received critical acclaim and has been assigned in classes at both Christian and secular universities (now in its Second Edition). He and his wife, Ginny, live in Houston, Texas.

_____

Notes

Notes for the Introduction

[1] There are numerous species of flightless birds that are commonly called penguins, and they do not all live in the extreme cold of the most southern regions. Some reside in temperate climates, even as far north as the Galápagos Islands. But all of today's penguins are found in the Southern Hemisphere.

[2] The 18 penguin species of the Southern Hemisphere all belong to the same family (Spheniscidae), while the great auk was from a different family (Alcidae) that includes puffins, guillemots, and razorbills, the great auk's closest living relative.

[3] Elizabeth Kolbert, *The Sixth Extinction: An Unnatural History*, (New York, 2014), pp. 57-59

[4] Ibid., p. 60

[5] Jeremy Gaskell, *Who Killed the Great Auk*, (New York, 2000), pp. 100, 113.

[6] Elizabeth Kolbert, *The Sixth Extinction: An Unnatural History*, (New York, 2014), p.65

[7] Neil Terblanche, "Barbaric elephant slaughter in Angola," *Africa Geographic,* July 25, 2016. Also, Jay Ross, "The Guns of Revolution Make War on Africa's Elephant Herds," *The Washington Post*, Dec. 13, 1982. Also, Siobhan O'Grady, "Thanks to Poachers, More African Elephants Are Being Killed than Born," *Foreign Policy*, March 3, 2016.

[8] Rachel Bale, "Critical Reefs Destroyed in Poacher's Quest for World's Biggest Clams," *National Geographic*, Aug. 30, 2016.

[9] Elizabeth Kolbert, *The Sixth Extinction: An Unnatural History*, (New York, 2014), pp. 107-108. Also see, Paul J. Crutzen, "Geology of mankind," *Nature* 415, p. 23, Jan. 3, 2002. Crutzen shared a Nobel Prize for his "work in atmospheric chemistry, particularly concerning the formation and decomposition of ozone." Particularly important was his discovery of the effects of ozone-depleting compounds.

[10] Robert Krulwich, "Big Fish Stories Getting Littler," *NPR*, Feb. 14, 2014.

[11] Hogs, domestic or wild, are not native to North America. They were originally brought to the Western Hemisphere by Christopher Columbus and his successors. Javelinas are distant relatives and are native to North America.

[12] Though commonly attributed to him, it is doubtful that Chief Seattle actually spoke those words. They have nevertheless been included here because they well reflect a widely held view among a number of Native American tribes concerning the symbiosis of humankind, other creatures, and the natural world.

Notes for Chapter 1—A Little Natural History

[1] "Why the Moon is getting further away from the Earth," *BBC Science*, July 19, 2011.

[2] The National Oceanic and Atmospheric Administration (NOAA), www.oceanservice.gov., U.S. Department of Commerce.

[3] Stephan Jay Gould, *Wonderful Life: The Burgess Shale and the Nature of History*, (New York 1989), pp. 57-58

[4] In the context of geologic time, "sudden" can mean over many millions of years. The so-called "Cambrian Explosion" is so named because a significant diversity of creatures *appears* suddenly in the fossil record. Many scientists theorize, however, that those creatures were the results of the evolution of ancestors over a very long period of time, but those soft-bodied ancestors were simply not preserved in the strata as fossils.

[5] A subsequent formation of the Appalachian Mountain range occurred later when North America collided with Africa (the supercontinent Gondwana at the time) to form the supercontinent Pangea, some 250 million years ago. Before erosion whittled them down, the Appalachians were as high as the Alps, the Himalayas, or the Rocky Mountains.

[6] Michael Greshko and the National Geographic staff, "What Are Mass Extinctions, and What Causes Them?", https://www.nationalgeographic.com/science/prehistoric-world/mass-extinction.html.

[7] Richard Fortey, *Life: A Natural History of the First Four Billion Years of Life on Earth*, (New York 1997), p. 141.

[8] Michael Greshko and the National Geographic staff, "What Are Mass Extinctions, and What Causes Them?", https://www.nationalgeographic.com/science/prehistoric-world/mass-extinction.html.

[9] Richard Fortey, *Life: A Natural History of the First Four Billion Years of Life on Earth*, (New York 1997), p. 166.

[10] Ibid., pp. 167, 177-8.

[11] Michael Greshko and the National Geographic staff, "What Are Mass Extinctions, and What Causes Them?", https://www.nationalgeographic.com/science/prehistoric-world/mass-extinction.html.

[12] Hillel J. Hoffman, "The Permian Extinction—When Life Nearly Came to an End," National Geographic, Thursday, June 6, 2019.

[13] Michael Greshko and the National Geographic staff, "What Are Mass Extinctions, and What Causes Them?", https://www.nationalgeographic.com/science/prehistoric-world/mass-extinction.html.

[14] Ibid.

[15] National Park Service website— https://www.nps.gov/bibe/learn/nature/pterosaur.htm.

[16] Ewen Callaway, "Did Humans Drive 'Hobbit' Species to Extinction?", *Nature*, March 30, 2016

[17] The demarcation of species is usually (but not always concretely) defined by two organisms' inability to produce fertile offspring. For example, horses and donkeys are separate species because their offspring—mules—are infertile. So, our cousin Neanderthals might be considered a sub-species. Gaia Vince refers to them, as well as Denisovans, as different "races" of humans.

[18] Jayne Wilkins, Benjamin J. Schoville, Kyle S. Brown, Michael Chazan, "Evidence for Early Hafted Hunting Technology," *Science*, Nov. 16, 2012, Vol. 338, Issue 6109, pp.942-946

Notes for Chapter 2—The Anthropocene Epoch

[1] While the domestication of agricultural livestock began around 10 or 11 thousand years ago, dogs were domesticated by at least 15,000 years ago, and perhaps much earlier. In addition to companionship, dogs were used as an alarm system and for hunting and fighting.

[2] Joe Pinkstone, "Scientists Declare Earth Has Entered the "Age of Man": Influential Panel Votes to Recognize the Start of the Anthropocene Epoch," *Mail Online*, 27 May, 2019.

[3] OurWorldinData.org, Based on estimates by *History database of the Global Environment* (HYDE) and the United Nations.

[4] Shreya Dasgupta, "Humans Have Been Transforming Earth for Thousands of Years, Study Finds," Mongabay News website, August 2019. Ms. Dasgupta was reporting on the findings of The ArchaeoGLOBE Project, a collaboration of 255 archaeologists from around the world.

[5] Gaia Vince, *Adventures in the Anthropocene: A Journey to the Heart of the planet We Made*, (Minneapolis, 2014), p. 339.

[6] Ashley Strickland, "Humans Have Been Impacting Earth for Thousands of Years, Study Finds," CNN, Published August 29, 2019.

[7] United States Census Bureau— https://www.census.gov/data/tables/time-series/demo/international-programs/historical-est-worldpop.html

[8] Benjamin Franklin lobbied for the turkey to become the official bird of the United States. Others thought the bald eagle was a better choice.

[9] J.R. McNeill, the Foreword to the 2003 publication of Alfred W. Crosby Jr.'s *The Columbian Exchange*, (Westport, CT 2003), p. xiii.

[10] The United States Library of Congress, "Immigration and Relocation in U.S. History."

[11] Elizabeth Kolbert, *The Sixth Extinction*, (New York, 2014), pp. 105-106.

[12] Camila Domonoske, "Call the Pied Piper: New Zealand Wants to Get Rid of Its Rats. All of Them," *NPR*, July 25, 2016.

[13] Harold D. Wallace, Jr., "Power from the People: Rural Electrification Brought More Lights," National Museum, of American History, February 12, 2016—https://americanhistory.si.edu/blog/rural-electrification

[14] NOAA, National Oceanic and Atmospheric Administration, United States Department of Commerce— https://oceanservice.noaa.gov/hazards/marinedebris/plastics-in-the-ocean.html

[15] Laura Parker, "Microplastics Found in 90 Percent of Table Salt," National Geographic, October 17, 2018. The study was widely reported in other publications as well.

[16] Rebecca Lindsay, United States National Oceanic and Atmospheric Administration (NOAA) website.

[17] David Shukman, "Brazil's Amazon: Deforestation 'Surges to 12-Year High'," BBC News, November 30, 2020.

[18] UNECE (United Nations Economic Commission for Europe) website—https://unece.org/challenge.

[19] Maryn McKenna, *National Geographic*, May 1, 2018, excerpted from her book, *Big Chicken: The Incredible Story of How Antibiotics Created Modern Agriculture and Changed the Way the World Eats*, (Washington DC, 2017)

[20] "The Broiler Chicken as a Signal of a Human Reconfigured Biosphere," a study published by Royal Society Open Science in November 2018, authored by Carys E. Bennett, Richard Tomas, Mark Williams, Jan Zalasiewicz, Matt Edgeworth, Holly Miller, Ben Coles, Alison Foster, Emily J. Burton, and Upenyu Marume.

[21] James Gorman, "It Could Be the Age of the Chicken, Geologically," New York Times, Dec. 11, 2018.

[22] *Bar-On YM, Milo R. Phillips, 2018 "The Biomass Distribution on Earth," Proc. National Academy of Science, USA 115, 6506-6511. (doi:10.1073/pnas.1711842115)*

[23] Given their chemistry, the incidences of chicken bones being fossilized will be few. The conditions within the landfilled in which they mostly reside, however, is quite conducive to mummification.

[24] Chickens were originally domesticated about 8,000 years ago in tropical South and Southeast Asia, from a bird called the red jungle fowl (*Gallus gallus*, Linnaeus, 1758). Red jungle fowl are found today in Africa, Europe, Australia, and the Americas, as a result of deliberate human translocation.

Notes for Chapter 3—Bring in the Crowd

[1] *Leviticus* 27: 3-7
[2] Steven Johnson, *Extra Life: A Short History of Living Longer*, (New York, 2021) p. 10
[3] Ibid., p. 18

4 The U.S. Food & Drug Administration—
https://www.fda.gov/food/consumers/food-loss-and-waste
5 David Wallace-Wells, The Uninhabitable Earth: Life After Warming,
(New York, 2020), p. 57.
6 Randy Moody, "The Truth About Republicans' Link with Planned
Parenthood," *Arizona Daily Star*, Jan. 22, 2016
7 Pema Levy, "How the Bush Family Aided Planned Parenthood's Rise,"
Mother Jones, Aug. 11, 2015
8 Fred Barnes, "Ronald Reagan, Father of the Pro-Life Movement," *Wall
Street Journal*, Nov. 6, 2003
9 "UNFPA Funding & Kemp-Kasten: An Explainer," Feb.3, 2021, Kaiser
Family Foundation.
10 Ibid.
11 Population growth in the United States has been augmented by
incoming immigrants since the founding of the nation. Illegal immigrants
often pay Social Security taxes, even though they will not receive benefits.
12 Anthony Cilluffo and Neil G. Ruiz, "World Population Is Projected to
Nearly Stop Growing by the End of the Century," *Fact-Tank: News in
Numbers*, June 17, 2019, Pew Research Center.
13 Joe Pinsker, "What Happens When the World's Population Stops
Growing?", *The Atlantic*, July 31, 2019.
14 Charles C. Mann, "Can Planet Earth Feed 10 Billion People?", March
2018, *The Atlantic*. Adapted from Mann's book, *The Wizard and the
Prophet: Two Remarkable Scientists and Their Dueling Visions to Shape
Tomorrow's World*, Penguin Random House, LLC, 2018.
15 *Africa Renewal* (an agency of the United Nations), "Desertification a
threat to Africa's development."
16 Charles C. Mann, "Can Planet Earth Feed 10 Billion People?", March
2018, *The Atlantic*. Adapted from Mann's book, *The Wizard and the
Prophet: Two Remarkable Scientists and Their Dueling Visions to Shape
Tomorrow's World*, (Penguin Random House, LLC, 2018).
17 Ibid.
18 Ibid.
19 Ibid.
20 The C4 Rice Project includes researchers from Academia Sinica,
Australian National University, Leibniz Institute of Plant Biochemistry,
Max Planck Institute of Molecular Plant Physiology, University of

Cambridge, University of Oxford, and Washington State University.

[21] The C4 Rice Project website—c4rice.com—University of Oxford, Department of Plant Sciences, Oxford, UK

[22] Anthony L. Contento, Ph.D. and Major David J. Stuckenberg, MPS, "Water Scarcity: The Most Understated Global Security Risk," *National Security Journal*, May 18, 2018, Harvard Law School.

[23] Peter Frankopan, *The Silk Roads: A New History of the World,* (New York, 2015), pp. 357-363.

[24] Gaia Vince, "Global Transformers: What If a Pandemic Strikes?", *BBC Future*, Smart Planet Series, July 10, 2013.

Notes for Chapter 4—The Sixth Extinction

[1] Ed Yong, The Origin of the Friendly Wolf that Confused Darwin," *National Geographic*, March 5, 2013.

[2] Ibid.

[3] Ibid.

[4] Charles Y. Feigin, Axel H. Newton, Liliya Doronina, Jürgen Schmitz, Christy A. Hipsley, Kieren J. Mitchell. Graham Gower, Bastien Llames, Julien Soubrier, Thomas N. Heider, Brandon R. Menzies, Alan Cooper, Rachel J. O'Neill, Andrew J. Pask, "Genome of the Tasmanian Tiger Provides Insights into the Evolution and Demography of an Extinct Marsupial Carnivore," *Nature Ecology & Evolution*, Open Access, Dec. 11, 2017.

[5] "Extinction of Thylacine," *National Museum of Australia*, Defining Moments

[6] Yuval Noah Harari, *Sapiens: A Brief History of Humankind*, (New York 2018), p. 72

[7] Ibid., pp. 70-71

[8] Ed Yong, "Mastodons Were Hunted in North America 800 Years Earlier Than Thought," *The Guardian*, Oct. 20, 2011.

[9] Brian Handwerk, "A Mysterious 25,000-Year-Old Structure Built of the Bones of 60 Mammoths," *Smithsonian Magazine*, March 16, 2020.

[10] Wayne Lynch, *Penguins of the World*, (Buffalo, N.Y., 2007), p. 162

[11] David Smits, "The Frontier Army and the Destruction of the Buffalo: 1856-1883," *Western Historical Quarterly. 25*, Sept. 1994.

[12] Dave Kindy, "How Buffalo Bill and a Civil War general saved Yellowstone National Park," The Washington Post, March 6, 2022.

[13] C. Gordon Hewitt, "The Coming Back of the Bison," *Natural History Magazine*, Dec. 1919.

[14] Loren McClenachan, "Documenting Loss of Large Trophy Fish from the Florida Keys with Historical Photographs," *Conservation Biology*, October 15, 2008

[15] Ibid.

[16] Ibid.

[17] Gaia Vince, "How the world's oceans could be running out of fish," *BBC Future*, Smart Planet Series, Sept. 20, 2012.

[18] Sylvia Earle, *The Sea Around Us*, Oxford University Press (New York, 2018), p. x

[19] Todd Woody, "The Sea Is Running Out of Fish, Despite Nation's Pledges to Stop It," *National Geographic*, October 8, 2019

[20] Gaia Vince, "How the World's Oceans Could Be Running Out of Fish," *BBC Future*, Smart Planet series, September 20, 2012

[21] Todd Woody, "The Sea Is Running Out of Fish, Despite Nation's Pledges to Stop It," *National Geographic*, October 8, 2019

[22] Ibid.

[23] NOAA website, "Ocean acidification."

[24] Mark Shwartz, "Ocean Ecosystems Plagued by Agricultural Runoff," *Stanford Report* (Stanford University), March 10, 2005

[25] Louise McRae, Stefanie Deinet, Valentina Marconi, Kate Scott-Gatty, and Robin Freeman, "The Living Planet Index: An Early Warning Indicator on the Health of Nature," *2020 Living Planet Report*. "The Living Planet Index (LPI) now tracks the abundance of almost 21,000 populations of mammals, birds, fish, reptiles and amphibians around the world."

[26] Stefanie Deinet and Louise McRae (ZSL), Paula Valdujo (WWF-Brazil) and Marcio Martins (Universidade de Sao Paulo), "Zooming in on Latin America and the Caribbean," *2020 Living Planet Report*.

[27] WWF (2020) *Living Planet Report 2020 - Bending the Curve of Biodiversity Loss*. Almond, R.E.A., Grooten M. and Petersen, T. (Eds). WWF, Gland, Switzerland.

[28] Sir Robert Watson, Tyndall Centre for Climate Change Research, "Biodiversity on the Brink: We Know It Is Crashing," *2020 Living Planet Report*.

[29] Seibold, S. Gossner, M.M., Simons, N.K., Blüthgen, N., Müller, J., *et al*

(2019) "Arthropod decline in grasslands and forests is associated with landscape-level drivers. *Nature 574*:671-674. doi: 10.38/s41586-019-1684.3.

[30] Peter Soroye, Tim Newbold, Jeremy Kerr, "Climate Change Contributes to Widespread Declines Among Bumble Bees Across Continents," *Science Magazine*, Feb. 7, 2020.

[31] Douglas Main, "Bumblebees Are Going Extinct in a Time of 'Climate Chaos'," *National Geographic*, Feb. 6, 2020.

[32] Stephan Leahy, "Polar Bears Really Are Starving Because of Global Warming, Study Shows, *National Geographic*, Feb. 1, 2018

[33] Ibid.

[34] Ibid.

[35] NASA, "Arctic Ice Minimum," *Global Climate Change*, May 14, 2021. Site Editor: Holly Shaftel; Managing Editor and Science Editor: Susan Callery; Senior Producer: Randal Jackson; Senior Science Editor: Daniel Bailey.

[36] Shaye Wolf, "Climate Change Threatens Penguins," *Action Bioscience*, Sept. 2009, American Institute of Biological Sciences.

[37] Ibid.

[38] Ibid.

[39] The Associated Press, "Plants Migrate North as Temperatures Rise," *CBS News*, June 26, 2008.

[40] Elizabeth Kolbert, *The Sixth Extinction*, (New York, 2014), p. 267

[41] Ibid., p. 268

Notes for Chapter 5—A Torrid Future

[1] Office of the Historian, United States State Department.

[2] Russia is rapidly militarizing the Arctic by building bases and testing its newest weapons there. The activity is, in part, associated with Vladimir Putin's intent to develop and control a key shipping route from Asia to Europe across the top of Siberia. Though the United States already has Thule Air Force Base above the Arctic circle in Greenland, owning the territory would provide the U.S. with much greater flexibility in the deployment of forces.

[3] Laura Geggel, "Trump Says He Wants to Buy Greenland. Here's Why." *Live Science*, 2019.

[4] David Herring, "Are there positive benefits from global warming?", *Climate.gov*, U.S. National Oceanic and Atmospheric Administration.

[5] Ask NASA Climate blog, Site Editor: Holly Shaftel, Managing Editor: Susan Callery, "There Is No Impending 'Mini Ice Age'," NASA, Feb. 13, 2020.

[6] Victoria Jaggard, *Science Executive Editor*, "The Big Topic: Buckle Up and Enjoy," *National Geographic*, May 19, 2021.

[7] Earth Science Communications Team at NASA's Jet Propulsion Laboratory, California Institute of Technology, "Warming Seas Are Accelerating Greenland's Glacier Retreat," Site Editor: Holly Shaftel, Managing Editor: Susan Callery NASA online, Jan. 25, 2021.

[8] Ibid.

[9] Associated Press, "Record melt: Greenland lost 586 billion tons of ice in 2019," *NBC News.com*, Aug. 21, 2020.

[10] Nicola Jones, "Polar Warning: Even Antarctica's Coldest Region Is Starting to Melt," *Yale Environment 360*, Yale University, March 28, 2019.

[11] Ibid.

[12] Rebecca Lindsey, "Climate Change: Global Sea Level," *Climate.gov, Science & Information for a Climate-Smart Nation*, NOAA, January 25, 2021.

[13] Katherina Buchholz, "Rising Sea Levels Will Threaten 200 Million People by 2100," Statisica.com.

[14] Jon Letman, "Rising seas give island nation a stark choice: relocate or elevate," *National Geographic*, Nov. 19, 2018.

[15] Tim Collins, "Rising sea levels will make low-lying atoll islands like the Seychelles and Maldives uninhabitable as soon as 2030," *The Daily Mail*, April 25, 2018.

[16] Rebecca Lindsey, "Climate Change: Global Sea Level," *Climate.gov, Science & Information for a Climate-Smart Nation*, NOAA, January 25, 2021.

[17] Aria Bendix, "8 American cities that could disappear by 2100," *Business Insider*, Mar. 17, 2020.

[18] Deborah Dardis and Pat Pendarvis, "Louisiana's disappearing WETLANDS," *Louisiana's Oil: Understanding the environmental and economic impact*, July 12, 2010, Southeastern Louisiana University.

[19] Virginia Hanusik, "Ecotourism could help the 'Amazon of North America' recover. Here's how," *National Geographic*, April 16, 2021.

[20] Deborah Dardis and Pat Pendarvis, "Louisiana's disappearing WETLANDS," *Louisiana's Oil: Understanding the environmental and*

economic impact, July 12, 2010, Southeastern Louisiana University.

[21] Bob Marshall, "New Research: Louisiana coast faces highest rate of sea-level rise worldwide," The Lens, Feb. 21, 2013.

[22] Fraser Cain, "Decreasing Earthshine Could Be Tied to Global Warming," *Universe Today*, May 27, 2004

[23] Gaia Vince, *Adventures in the Anthropocene: A Journey to the Heart of the Planet We Made*, (Minneapolis, 2014), pp. 64-69.

[24] Ibid., p. 65.

[25] Ibid., pp. 62-64

[26] Alejandra Borunda, "The last five years were the hottest ever recorded," *National Geographic*, Feb. 6, 2019.

[27] David Wallace-Wells, *The Uninhabitable Earth: Life After Warming*, (New York, 2019, 2020), pp. 73-74

[28] Terri Adams-Fuller, "Extreme Heat is Deadlier Than Hurricanes, Floods and Tornadoes Combined," *Scientific American Magazine*, July 2023

[29] Cheryl Katz, Will Global Warming Heat Us Beyond Our Physical Limits," *National Geographic*, Dec. 15, 2015.

[30] *Guinness World Records*, "Deadliest Heat Waves."

[31] Victoria Bekiempis, "Record-breaking US Pacific north-west heatwave killed almost 200 people," The Guardian, July 8, 2021.

[32] David Wallace-Wells, *The Uninhabitable Earth: Life After Warming*, (New York, 2019, 2020), p. 46.

[33] Vaidyanathan A., Malilay J., Schramm P., Saha S., "Heat-Related Deaths—United States, 2004-2018." MMWR Morb Mortal Wkly Rep 2020; 69:729-734. DOI, CDC.

[34] Dino Grandoni and Brady Dennis, "U.S. has entered unprecedented climate territory, EPA warns," *The Washington Post*, May 12, 2021.

[35] Linda Givetash, "Australian wildfires declared among the worst wildlife disasters in modern history," *NBC News*, July 28, 2020.

[36] Nathaniel Gronewold, "Smoke from Australia's Bushfires Killed Hundreds," *Scientific American Magazine*, March 24, 2020.

[37] Dani Anguiano, "California's wildfire hell: how 2020 became the state's worst ever fire season," *The Guardian*, Dec. 30, 2020.

[38] Alex Wigglesworth, "California wildfires on the cusp of burning 4 million acres so far this year," *Los Angeles Times*, Oct. 3, 2020.

[39] Dani Anguiano, "California's wildfire hell: how 2020 became the state's worst ever fire season," *The Guardian*, Dec. 30, 2020.

[40] Darrell Smith, "'These are hidden deaths.' Over 1,000 likely died early due to California's wildfire smoke," *The Sacramento Bee*, September 23, 2020.

[41] Daoping Wang, Dabo Guan, Shupeng Zhu, Michael MacKinnon, Guannan Geng, Qiang Zhang, Heran Zheng, Tianyang Lei, Shuai Shao, Peng, Gong, & Steven J. Davis, "Economic footprint of California wildfires in 2018," Published in *Nature Sustainability*, Dec. 7, 2020.

[42] Shelly Sommer, Institute of Arctic and Alpine Research, University of Colorado Boulder, and Susan Meikle, Miami University News, "Miami fire scientist: "Zombie fires" one of the new features driving Arctic fires," *Miami University News*, Oct. 6, 2020.

[43] Alejandra Borunda, "'Zombie' fires in the Arctic are linked to climate change," *National Geographic*, May 19, 2021.

[44] USDA, "Changing Climate Is Affecting Agriculture in the U.S." www.usda.gov/topics/climate-solutions.

[45] CSSR Report, "Chapter 7: Precipitation Change in the Unites States," *Climate Science Special Report*, U.S. National Climate Assessment 4

[46] Diana Leonard, "Southwest drought is the most extreme in 1,200 years, study finds," *The Washington Post*, February 14, 2022.

[47] National Immigration Forum, "Push and Pull Factors: What Drives Central American Migrants to the U.S.?" July 23, 2019

[48] Kimberly M.S. Cartier, "Climate Change Uproots Global Agriculture," *EOS*, Jan. 25, 2021. (*EOS* is a publication of the AGU—American Geophysical Union.)

Notes for Chapter 6—Are We to Blame?

[1] Nick Gass, "Bush super PAC hammers Trump on getting military advise from 'the shows'," *Politico*, Dec. 12, 2015. Also see, Justin Baragona, "Trump Admits He Sits Around Watching Cable News All Night," *The Daily Beast*, Sep. 10, 2020.

[2] Jessica Merzdorf, "New Studies Increase Confidence in NASA's Measure of Earth's Temperature," *Global Climate Change*, May 23, 2019, NASA.

[3] "Greenland. Antarctic Melting Six Times Faster Than in the 1990s," *Global Climate Change: Vital Signs of the Planet*, NASA, March 15,2020. www.climate.nasa.gov.

[4] Rebecca Hersher, "Earth is Barreling Toward 1.5 Degrees Celsius of

Warming, Scientists warn," May 26, 2021, *NPR.*

[5] Kathryn Hansen, "Water Vapor Confirmed as Major Player in Climate Change," Nov. 17, 2008, NASA's Goddard Space Flight Center.

[6] Overview of Greenhouse Gases, U.S. Environmental Protection Agency, www.epa.gov.

[7] Amy Dusto, "Climate at the Core: how scientists study ice cores to reveal Earth's climate history," *Climate.gov.* U.S. National Oceanic and Atmospheric Administration.

[8] William Ferguson, "Ice Core Data Help Solve a Global Warming Mystery," *Scientific American*, March 1, 2013.

[9] Brady Dennis and Steven Mufson, "Despite pandemic, level of carbon dioxide in the atmosphere hits historic levels," *Washington Post*, June 7, 2021.

[10] Ibid.

[11] Ibid.

[12] Brady Dennis and Sarah Kaplan, "Humans have pushed the climate into 'unprecedented' territory, landmark U.N. report finds," *The Washington Post*, August 9, 2021.

[13] Ibid.

[14] Ibid.

Notes for Chapter 7—An Age of Unreason

[1] The Associated Press, published by *NBC News*, Feb 17, 2021

[2] Shawn Mulchy, "Many Texans Have Died Because of the Winter Storm. Just How Many Won't Be Known for Weeks or Months," *The Texas Tribune*, February 19, 2021

[3] Ariana Garcia, "Texas officials add 36 more deaths to February 2021 winter storm," *The Houston Chronicle*, Jan. 3, 2022

[4] Eric Bradner, "Texas Republicans Criticized for Misleading Claims that Renewable Energy Sources Caused Massive Outages," *CNN*, Feb. 18, 2021

[5] Ibid.

[6] For a thorough discussion of the intersection of science and religion, see the book, *Exploring Faith and Reason: The Reconciliation of Christianity and Biological Evolution.*

[7] Richard Hofstadter, *Social Darwinism in American Thought*, (Philadelphia 1944, republished by Beacon Press in 1992), p. 41

[8] Albert Mohler, "Relativity, Moral Relativism, and the Modern Age,"

Commentary Dec. 7, 2015, www.albertmohler.com.

[9] *Britannica*, "Intellectual and Cultural Impact of Relativity"

[10] Ibid.

[11] Shawn Otto, *The War on Science: Who's Waging It, Why It Matters, What We Can Do About It*, (Minneapolis 2016), p. 103

[12] Ibid., p. 151-152

[13] Ibid., p. 153

[14] There are limits the hard news division's permission to tell the truth. When FOX News was the first network to accurately call Arizona for Joe Biden in the 2020 election, it was an impressive scoop resulting from superior analytical analysis. But, since it did not fit with the disinformation narrative FOX was promoting for Donald Trump, those responsible were fired.

[15] Jamie Smyth, "Murdoch's News Corp Accused of Undermining Democracy," *The Financial Times*, April 12, 2021

[16] Janes C. Timm, "Sidney Powell's legal defense: 'Reasonable people' wouldn't believe her election fraud claims," *NBC News*, March 23, 2021

[17] Christopher Keating, "Quinnipiac Poll: 77% of Republicans believe there was widespread fraud in the presidential election; 60% overall consider Joe Biden's victory legitimate," *Hartford Courant*, Dec. 10, 2020

[18] Jeff Seldin, "Trump Fires Security Chief Who Said 2020 Vote Was 'Most Secure' in US History," *VOA*, Nov. 18, 2020.

[19] Conservapedia, under the heading, "Counterexamples to Relativity."

[20] Elizabeth Dwoskin, "Misinformation on Facebook got six times more clicks than factual news during the 2020 election, study finds," *The New York Times*, Sept. 4, 2021.

[21] Guillaume Chaslot, "The Toxic Potential of YouTube's Feedback Loop," *Wired Magazine*, July 13, 2019.

[22] M. Best, A. Katamba, and D. Neuhauser, "Making the Right Decision: Benjamin Franklin's son dies of smallpox in 1736," US National Library of Medicine, National Institutes of Health, Dec. 2007.

[23] Shawn Otto, *The War on Science: Who's Waging It, Why It Matters, What We Can Do About It*, (Minneapolis 2016), p. 140

[24] Ibid.

[25] Doyle McManus, "Half of Republican men say they don't want a vaccine. They're mooching off the rest of us," *Los Angeles Times*, March 21, 2021

[26] Dan Balz and Emily Guskin, "Post-ABC poll: Biden earns high marks for handling the pandemic, but many Republicans resist vaccination," *The Washington Post*, July 4, 2021.

27 Julian Mark, "Conservative radio host said he constantly hugged strangers to catch COVID," *Washington Post*, October 19, 2021.

28 Elizabeth Chuck, "Science says fluoride in water is good for kids. So why are these towns banning it?", *NBC News*, Oct. 17, 2018.

29 Wieczorek, A. M. and Wright, M.G. (2012) History of Agricultural Biotechnology: How Crop Development Has Evolved. *Nature Education Knowledge* 3(10):9

30 Bill Prochnau and Valerie Thomas, "The Watt Controversy," *The Washington Post*, June 30, 1981.

31 Media Transparency, 2007.

32 Bill Prochnau and Valerie Thomas, "The Watt Controversy," *The Washington Post*, June 30, 1981.

33 Fred Krupp, "The Environmental Legacy of President George H.W. Bush," Dec. 1, 2018, *Environmental Defense Fund* website.

34 Scott Waldman, "Bush Had a Lasting Impact on Climate and Air Policy," *E&E News, Scientific American*, Dec. 3, 2018

35 Suzanne Goldenberg, "The worst of times: Bush's environmental legacy examined," *The Guardian*, Jan. 16, 2009.

36 Ibid.

37 Ibid.

38 Ibid.

39 Ibid.

40 Justin Baragona, "Trump Admits He Sits Around Watching Cable News All Night," *The Daily Beast*, Sep. 10, 2020. Also see, Nick Gass, "Bush super PAC hammers Trump on getting military advise from 'the shows'," Politico, Dec. 12, 2015.

41 Separate studies are described in these two articles: "Is News Corp. Failing Science?" by the Union of Concerned Scientists --- Lindsay Abrams, "Watching Fox News makes people distrust science," *Salon*, Aug.6, 2013.

42 Jeffrey Mervis, "Trump has shown little respect for U.S. science. So why are some parts thriving?" *Science Magazine*, Oct. 14, 2020.

43 Madeline Carlisle, "Newly-Released NOAA Emails Show Anger and Confusion Around Trump's 'Doctored' Hurricane Dorian Map," *Time Magazine*, Feb. 1, 2020

44 Jeffrey Mervis, "Trump has shown little respect for U.S. science. So why are some parts thriving?", *Science Magazine*, Oct. 14, 2020.

45 Frank Morris, "USDA Research Agencies 'Decimated" By Forced Move.

Undoing the Damage Won't Be Easy," *NPR*, Feb. 2, 2021.

[46] Lisa Friedman, "E.P.A. to Review Attacks on Science Under Trump, *New York Times*, March 24,2021

[47] Lisa Friedman, "Bipartisan Report Says Trump's Abuse Has Pushed Federal Science to a 'Crisis'," *New York Times*, Oct. 3, 2019.

[48] Ibid.

[49] Dan Diamond, "Trump officials celebrated efforts to change CDC reports on coronavirus, emails show," *The Washington Post*, April 9, 2021

[50] Robert Costa and Philip Rucker, "Woodward book: Trump says he knew coronavirus was 'deadly' and worse than the flu while intentionally misleading Americans," *The Washington Post*, Sept. 9, 2020.

[51] Igor Derysh, "Deborah Birx says Trump's COVID response may have cost 400,000 lives: Did she do enough?", *Salon*, March 29,2021.

[52] Marcia McNutt, President of the National Academy of Sciences, and Victor J. Dzau. President of the National Academy of Medicine, "NAS and NAM Presidents Alarmed by Political Interference in Science Amid Pandemic," *The National Academies of Sciences, Engineering, Medicine*, September 24, 2020

Notes for Chapter 8—A Bit of Hope

[1] Sarah Gardner, "LA Smog: the battle against air pollution," *Marketplace.org*, July 14,2014

[2] "Progress Cleaning the Air and Improving People's Health," *Clean Air Act Overview*, U.S. Environmental Protection Agency.

[3] David Keiser and Joseph S. Shapiro, "How the Clean Water Act has served the environment and the economy," *VOX, CEPR Policy Portal*, Oct. 24, 2018.

[4] Kara Manke, "Clean Water Act dramatically cut pollution in U.S. waterways," *Berkley News*, Oct. 2018.

[5] David Keiser and Joseph S. Shapiro, "How the Clean Water Act has served the environment and the economy," *VOX, CEPR Policy Portal*, Oct. 24, 2018.

[6] Kara Manke, "Clean Water Act dramatically cut pollution in U.S. waterways," *Berkley News*, Oct. 2018.

[7] Ryan Beam, "Analysis: 85 Percent of Continental U.S. Birds Protected by Endangered Species Act Have Increased or Stabilized Since Being Protected," *Center for Biological Diversity*, June 21, 2016

[8] "History of Bald Eagle Decline, Protection and Recovery," U.S. Fish & Wildlife Service.

[9] "The Endangered Species Act: A Wild Success," *Center for Biological Diversity*

[10] United States Department of State, *Office of Environmental Quality* website, "The Montreal Protocol on Substances That Deplete the Ozone Layer."

[11] Ibid.

[12] Neal E. Boudette and Coral Davenport, "G.M. Announcement Shakes Up U.S. Automaker's Transition to Electric Cars," *The New York Times*, Jan. 29, 2021.

[13] Ibid.

[14] Andrew Winston, "Inside UPS's electric vehicle strategy," *Longitudes*, UPS, April 9, 2018. (Originally published in *Harvard Business Review*.)

[15] Ibid.

[16] Gavin Bade, "The oil industry vs. the electric car," *Politico*, Sept. 16, 2019.

[17] Josie Garthwaite, "Stanford study finds stark differences in the carbon-intensity of global oil fields," *Stanford News*, Stanford University, Aug. 30, 2018.

[18] Alex Kimani, "Which Oil Major is Winning the Race to Net Zero Emissions?" *OilPrice.com*, Sept. 10, 2020.

[19] The catchphrase was derived from a quote by Gordon Gekko, a character in the 1987 movie, "Wall Street." The actual line is, "greed, for lack of a better word, is good. Greed is right. Greed works..."

[20] Tom Wilson (CEO of Allstate Corp.), "How corporations can be a force for good," an op-ed in *The Washington Post*, Sept. 29, 2016.

[21] Ibid.

[22] Isabelle Rodd, "Climate change: The craft brewery using algae to cut emissions," *BBC News* / Australia, July 6, 2021.

[23] bcorporation.net

[24] Melina Theodorou, "15 Awesome Environmentally Friendly Companies," *CareerAddict*, Feb. 15, 2020.

[25] Stephen Humphries, "Got milk? Nope. Dairy-free ice cream is filling up freezers," *The Christian Science Monitor*, Aug. 20,2021.

[26] Tim Searchinger, Craig Hanson, Richard Waite, and Janet Ranganathan, "10 Breakthrough Technologies Can Help Feed the World Without Destroying It," *World Resources Report: Creating a Sustainable Food Future*, World Resources Institute, in association with the World Bank, UN Environment Program and UN Development Program, July 17, 2019.

[27] Ibid.

[28] Melissa Clark, "Sea Scallops Farmed in Maine Aren't Just Sustainable. They're Helping Their Habitat." *The New York Times*, Aug. 23, 2021.

[29] Susie Arnold, "Celebrate the planet, eat kelp," *The Island Institute*, April 19, 2021.

[30] Melissa Clark, "The Climate-Friendly Vegetable You Ought to Eat," *The New York Times*, April 30, 2019.

[31] Jim Morrison, "Turning manure into money," *The Washington Post*, June 16, 2020.

[32] Tim Searchinger, Craig Hanson, Richard Waite, and Janet Ranganathan, "10 Breakthrough Technologies Can Help Feed the World Without Destroying It," *World Resources Report: Creating a Sustainable Food Future*, World Resources Institute, in association with the World Bank, UN Environment Program and UN Development Program, July 17, 2019.

[33] Diane Nelson, "Feeding Cattle Seaweed Reduces Their Greenhouse Gas Emissions 82 Percent," *UC Davis News*, March 17, 2021.

[34] Ibid.

[35] Agnieszka de Sousa, "Cargill Backs Cow Masks to Trap Methane Burps," *Bloomberg News*, May 31, 2021.

[36] "Cows toilet trained to reduce greenhouse gas emissions," *BBC News*, Europe, Sept. 14, 2021.

[37] 10 Breakthrough Technologies Can Help Feed the World Without Destroying It," *World Resources Report: Creating a Sustainable Food Future*, World Resources Institute, in association with the World Bank, UN Environment Program and UN Development Program, July 17, 2019.

[38] Kate Selig, "Toxic 'forever chemicals' taint nearly half of U.S. tap water, study estimates," *The Washington Post*, July 7, 2023

[39] National Academies of Sciences, Engineering, and Medicine. 2019. *Negative Emissions Technologies and Reliable Sequestration: A Research Agenda*. Washington, DC: The National Academies Press. https://doi.org.

[40] Frank Swain, "The device that reverses CO2 emissions," *BBC Future*, March 11, 2021.

[41] Lindsey McGinnis, "Counting bees, growing trees: How people's efforts build back environments," *The Christian Science Monitor*, May 25, 2021.

[42] "Redbird Reef," *Atlas Obscura*

[43] Lindsey McGinnis, "Counting bees, growing trees: How people's efforts build back environments," *The Christian Science Monitor*, May 25, 2021.

[44] Ibid.

[45] Ibid.

[46] The editors of *E Magazine*, "What are Cities Doing to Go "Green?", as publish in *Scientific American*, March 11, 2009, and *The Christian Science Monitor*, March 13, 2009.

[47] Colin Arnold Dalrymple, "EU Funds for Hydrogen Buses in Iceland," *The Reykjavik Grapevine*, Oct. 10, 2018.

[48] The editors of *E Magazine*, "What are Cities Doing to Go "Green?", as publish in *Scientific American*, March 11, 2009, and *The Christian Science Monitor*, March 13, 2009.

[49] Clark Wilson, "Greening America's Communities," *U.S. Environmental Protection Agency*.

Notes for Addendum B—Our Carbon Footprint

[1] The Carbon Trust (2012) Carbon Footprint.

[2] "Carbon Footprint Factsheet," Pub. No. CSS09-05, *Center for Sustainable Systems*, University of Michigan, 2020.

[3] "Emissions & Generation Resource Integrated Database (eGRID)," U.S. EPA (2020).

[4] "Inventory of U.S. Greenhouse Gas Emissions and Sinks 1990-2018," U.S. EPA (2020).

[5] "Electric Power Monthly with Data from Feb. 2020," U.S. Energy Information Administration (EIA) 2020.

[6] "Inventory of U.S. Greenhouse Gas Emissions and Sinks 1990-2018)" U.S. EPA (2020).

[7] "Annual Energy Outlook 2020," U.S. EIA (2020).

[8] "Residential Energy Consumption Survey 2015," U.S. EIA (2020).

[9] "Benefits of Using Cold Water for Everyday Laundry in the U.S.," Mars C., (2016)

[10] "The EPA Automotive trends Report: Greenhouse Gas Emissions, Fuel Economy, and Technology since 1975," U.S. EPA (2020).

[11] *Transportation Energy Data Book: Edition 38.1*, U.S. Department of Energy, Oak Ridge National Lab (2020).

[12] "Emissions & Generation Resource Integrated Database (eGRID)," U.S. EPA (2020).

[13] "Life Cycle Assessment in the Automobile Sector: A Comparative Case Study of Internal Combustion Engine and Electric Car," Pero, F. et al. (2018).

[14] "how Much Carbon Dioxide is Produced by Burning Gasoline and Diesel Fuel," U.S. EIA (2016).

[15] "Fuel Properties Comparison Chart," U.S. Department of Energy (DOE), Alternative Fuels Data Center (2015).

[16] "The EPA Automotive trends Report: Greenhouse Gas Emissions, Fuel Economy, and Technology since 1975," U.S. EPA (2020).

[17] "Driving More Efficiently," U.S. DOE, Office of Energy Efficiency and Renewable Energy (EERE) (2020).

[18] "Inventory of U.S. Greenhouse Gas Emissions and Sinks 1990-2018)" U.S. EPA (2020).

[19] Ibid.

[20] "Quantifying Carbon Footprint Reduction Opportunities for U.S. Households and Communities," Jones C., Kammen D. (2011).

[21] Boehm R., et al, "A Comprehensive Life Cycle Assessment of Greenhouse Gas Emissions from U.S. Household Food Choices." (2018).

[22] "Inventory of U.S. Greenhouse Gas Emissions and Sinks 1990-2018)" U.S. EPA (2020)

[23] Weber, C. and H. Matthews, "Food Miles and the Relative Climate Impacts of Food Choices in the United States." (2008).

[24] Heller, M., et al., "Implications of Future US Diet Scenarios on Greenhouse gas Emissions," (2020)

[25] Weber, C. and H. Matthews, "Food Miles and the Relative Climate Impacts of Food Choices in the United States." (2008).

[26] Heller, M.C., et al. (2018). "Greenhouse gas emissions and energy use associated with production of individual self-selected US diets." Environmental Research Letters, 13(4), 044004.

Index

Printed in Great Britain
by Amazon

35982919R00128